T R I C K S   2

Another 125 Ways to Make Good Sex Better

T R I C K S   2

**Another** *125 Ways to Make Good Sex Better*

by Jay Wiseman

Greenery
Press

Published in the United States by Greenery Press, 3739 Balboa Ave. #195, San Francisco, CA 94121.

ISBN #0-9639763-3-8

ISBN 0-9639763-3-8

51195>

9 780963 976338

Table of Contents

Warning and Disclaimer 1
Creative Thinking, Medicine, Sex, and Me 3
So Why Am I Writing a Second "Tricks" Book? 5
Assumptions 7
The Purposes of Tricks 10
The Limits Of Tricks 12
A Few Don'ts Regarding Tricks (and Other Matters) 14
Intoxicants 16
TRICKS 2 17
Spanking Tricks – And A Few Related Others 65
Condoms, Gloves, And Other Goodies 78
Sex, Risk, Probability, and Political Correctness 82
Lubricants – Advantages, Disadvantages, And Dangers 87
What To Do If A Condom Fails 90
What To Do for a Contaminated Skin Break 93
A Warning About SM 96
An Even Stronger Warning About Breath Control Play 102
Problems 105
Alternative Sexuality Resources 111
Bibliography 117
Please Send Me Your Tricks (but read this carefully first) 120
Other Publications from Greenery Press 122

Acknowledgements (The "Thank You" List)

While I promised not to attribute a particular Trick to a particular person or persons (also, it wasn't rare for a Trick to be independently suggested by more than one individual), all the folks listed below contributed at least one Trick, or other useful information, to this book. Thanks, everybody!

Ava Taurel
Ann Grogan
Annagreta Carver
Anonymous
Bart
Beau
Carol Queen
Cecelia Tan
Clark Taylor
Dolores Bishop
Dossie Easton
Jaymes Easton
Francesca Guido
Gianna
Gillian
Good Vibrations Tricks
  Brainstorming Group
Informed Sources

Janet Hardy
Jack F.
Katie Karlsson
Lani Ka'ahumanu
Maria Isaacs
Mic Bergen
No names, please!
nosferatu1@aol.com
Passionflower Tricks
  Brainstorming Group
RD
Richard Beavereater
Sage
The Retired Courtesan (bless her
  heart)
Tom Burns
Wally and Louisa Daniels
Walter Shelburne

Warning and Disclaimer

Let us understand that engaging in sexual activity always includes some degree of risk. If done in the right way, at the right time, with the right person, in the right location, and for the right reasons, sex can be one of the most wonderful experiences possible – a foretaste of heaven.

If any of the above is not right, the results can range from unpleasant to disastrous. Improper sexual conduct can result in (among many other things), unplanned pregnancy, getting a fatal sexually transmitted disease, sterility, destruction of a relationship, imprisonment, suicide, and murder.

Erotic energy is one of the most powerful forces that act upon living things. Respect, honor, and pay attention to that power and you can experience bliss. Disrespect or ignore that power and you might not live to regret it.

The primary purpose of "Tricks 2" is to provide information and advice that will help make good sex between informed, consenting adults a little bit better. It also provides basic information to help people understand their situations, make them aware of possible alternatives, cope with problems, and find helpful resources.

Please do not think of this book as any kind of medical, legal, psychological, or other professional advice. It most certainly in not intended as a substitute for proper sex therapy. Most of its core information (particularly the "Tricks" themselves) was discovered on my own, taught to me by lovers I have had, shared with me by friends during highly informal conversations (many has been the occasion since "Tricks" was published that someone has come up to me and said "I've got a Trick for you"), or sent to me in the mail. Please keep that in mind when considering this book's contents.

Almost without question, there are at least a few factual errors in this book, and probably a few typographical errors as well. Also, it's very common, in this and many other fields, that information believed accurate at the time of publication is later revealed to be inaccurate – sometimes only slightly so, sometimes very much so. If you have even the slightest question about the accuracy or safety of anything in here, please check with independent sources. If their recommendations differ from mine, please let me know. By the way, please remember that not all professional advice is equally complete, accurate, up to date, and unbiased. By all means get an independent "second opinion" (and maybe a "third opinion") if you feel even the slightest need for it.

No one associated with writing, editing, printing, distributing, or selling this book, or in any other way associated with it, is in any way liable for damages that result from acting on the information herein. While I have most certainly not put anything in here that I believe would cause harm, understand clearly that you act on the information in this book entirely at your own risk.

Creative Thinking, Medicine, Sex, and Me

For about the last ten years, I've been fascinated by "thinking skills" such as decision-making, problem-solving, creative thinking, and so forth. I first became seriously interested when I was in medical school, and saw how crucial the ability to make good decisions was to the effective and compassionate practice of medicine. Sadly, entirely too much of my education in this regard was obtained by seeing the results of bad decisions.

I learned that decision-making could be studied as a discipline in itself, standing apart from the subject of the decisions. I began to study it in an earnest way, and the resulting effects on my life have been profound. Among other things, I eventually decided that it would be best for me to leave the medical profession. (This was not the first time in my life, nor was it the last, that I applied a subject beyond what my teachers intended.)

My study of decision-making led me to study larger topics such as problem-solving, brainstorming, and the many books on thinking skills, including some written by Dr. Edward de Bono.

During recent years, in addition to reading extensively on these topics, I've attended regular meetings of a brainstorming group, co-sponsored a series of presentations for San Francisco Mensa called "Thinking About Thinking," taken classes and workshops on de Bono's thinking skills, studied a bit of improv theater, worked with computer "idea processing" software, played board games dealing with creative thinking, and done a few other things.

Frankly, I've had a ball. For me, learning new thinking skills is a joy. I've also learned something about how important these skills are. Thinking skills should be taught much more extensively and intensively than they currently are, starting in grade school.

One thinking skill taught by Dr. de Bono is that it is often possible to make greater gains in a given situation by improving what is already working well than it is by fixing problems. For example, a store in financial trouble can often do better by increasing sales than by cutting costs.

I took that thinking and applied it to sex. It hit me almost immediately that many of my past lovers had "a certain thing" (or two, or three, or...) that they did with their hand, mouth, or other body part, or that they had a certain way of arranging things, or that they did something else that contributed wonderfully to something that was already going pretty good. (I had come up with a few of my own.) What was done could be described to and shared with others, and so I decided to do that.

I named them "Tricks," wrote down about 125 of them, included other information that I thought would be useful, and put it out as the first "Tricks" book. It turned out to be a very popular idea. The book sold well, and enough people sent in Tricks of their own to make a second book possible – and here it is.

Like the first "Tricks" book, this book starts with the assumption that you already have a good relationship with your sexual partner and goes on from there. Also like the first "Tricks" book, it includes basic referral information if the above assumption is not the case.

So Why Am I Writing a Second "Tricks" Book?

Well, here I go again. Perhaps I should say here *you* go again, for reader contribution accounts for much more of the contents of this book than was true of the first "Tricks" book.

I must say it has been interesting living with the results of the first "Tricks" book. For one thing, it turned out to be far more popular than I expected. For another, the Tricks that people have sent me in the mail have been wonderful to read. (This is not to mention the scandalous "Tricks brainstorming sessions." Perhaps the less said about those events the better, you scamps!)

There is an incredible amount of erotic knowledge and wisdom out there and, in truth, I feel a bit humbled to have been entrusted with communicating a portion of it to you. The responsible sharing of erotic pleasure with another adult can deepen and strengthen relationships, calm and soothe troubled souls, relax tense bodies, build genuine intimacy, and help restore peace of mind. It can also, of course, be very, very hot and passionate. Not to mention a great deal of fun!

"Tricks 2" is my fifth book on topics dealing with relationships and sexuality, and I've learned a few important things during the process of writing them.

Perhaps the major lesson for me has been that everybody, and I mean everybody, struggles with sex. It's a part of life that just doesn't behave itself all that well, for very long, for most people. In writing these "Tricks" books, I have learned that I'm sharing information that will significantly help many, many people with a difficult, often *very* difficult, part of their lives.

I've been particularly gratified that people responded well to the "satellite" information provided in addition to the Tricks themselves. I've also felt somewhat alarmed that the sex education information I included turned out to be as needed as it was. The degree of "sexual illiteracy" in this country, and the very unfortunate, sometimes even tragic, consequences thereof are sobering to contemplate.

Other than the Tricks themselves, there is a certain amount of duplication of material between this book and the first "Tricks" book, particularly the referral information. I apologize for that, but there are only so many significantly different ways of presenting such material. Please bear with me, and understand that all-too-many of my readers will need such information all-too-desperately.

If my "Tricks" books help even slightly in preventing unplanned pregnancies, in slowing the spread of sexually transmitted diseases, and in encouraging people to be more considerate, responsible, consensual, and honorable regarding their sexual behavior, then these books will be very successful indeed.

Assumptions

In presenting the material in this book, I am making the following assumptions about your situation. If these assumptions are not true in your case, please adjust your behavior accordingly.

I'm assuming:

1. That both of you are willing (and, hopefully, eager) to have sex with each other. Consent is absolutely essential.

2. That having sex with each other will not violate any agreements you made with other people about your sexual conduct.

3. That both of you understand the nature of what you are doing. Having sex with someone too young, feeble-minded, senile, intoxicated, or otherwise unable to reasonably understand and consent to what is happening may get you charged with rape, even if no force or threat of force was used. Remember, if they're too drunk to drive, they're probably too drunk to have sex.

4. That both of you have reached the age of consent in your state (and that you live in the United States). I believe the age of consent is as low as 12 in at least one state and as high as 18 in many others. Remember, an act that is perfectly legal on one side of a state line might get you a lengthy prison sentence on the other side. Make sure you know the age of consent in your state.

Your local library should have a copy of your state's criminal code in its reference section. Reading its sections on rape, incest, indecent exposure, lewd and lascivious conduct, assault, contributing to the delinquency of a minor, and related sections may be very informative. Asking a local attorney or police officer (that you already know well) can also help, but remember that opinions, knowledge, and objectivity can vary widely, even among such "experts." Try to talk to more than one source.

(By the way, sex between blood relatives may be illegal no matter what the age of those involved. If you cannot legally marry a particular person, it may also be illegal for you to have sex with them. This could be true even if both of you are over 18 and both fully consent.)

5. That the acts I'm describing are legal in your state. Although the laws are rarely enforced, oral sex, anal intercourse, and other practices are still a crime in some states, even if done by consenting adults in private. Find out your state's laws and, where appropriate, work to change them.

    As you can see, this whole area is badly in need of enlightened legislative reform.

6. That there is no risk of passing on any sexually transmitted disease. If such a risk does exist, please modify what you do. Among other things, if you have herpes or have tested positive for the AIDS virus and have sex with someone without first telling them about that, you could be arrested. You could also be sued if your partner becomes infected.

If you have any questions, one resource is the National Sexually Transmitted Disease Hotline at (800) 227-8922.

The Purposes of Tricks

The purposes of "Tricks" (the books) as well as Tricks (the activities) are sevenfold:

1.   To increase the amount of erotic pleasure my readers share with their partners.

2.   To combat sexual illiteracy, a condition that creates untold heartache, frustration, and life-altering mishaps.

3.   To reduce sexually transmitted diseases and unplanned pregnancies.

4.   To promote high ethics, personal responsibility, and informed consent regarding sexual behavior.

5.   To affirm that sexuality is an honored and honorable part of our lives.

6.   To increase communication between partners.

7.   To encourage the enactment of saner and more appropriate laws.

Criteria

For inclusion in this book, a Trick usually had to meet the following criteria:

1.   It had to be something that could be done pretty much on impulse in the here and now. Nothing too elaborate.

2.   It had to involve minimal equipment, preferably nothing outside the bodies of the people involved. If it did involve equipment, it couldn't be "formal" sexual equipment (that's the subject of my next book, "Sex Toy Tricks"). For this "Tricks" book, any external item usually had to be something found in the average household.

3.   It had to be safe. I included nothing I thought likely to endanger people.

4.   It had to pertain directly to sex or a very closely related matter.

5.   It had to have a successful track record. I looked for tricks that had consistently made more than one lover gasp, moan, or sigh. (I have come to think of this as a high F.A.Q. or "flop-around quotient.")

6.   It had to appeal to a wide, mainstream audience. The trick couldn't be too far out or kinky. (That's another book.) Most of the tricks therefore, involve masturbation, fellatio, cunnilingus, vaginal intercourse, or anal intercourse.

A New Category Of Tricks

Based on the criteria described above, trends in popular culture, my published writings since the last "Tricks" book, the persuasion of my friends, and an enormous amount of thinking about it, I have decided to slightly enlarge the scope of Tricks to include activities that may involve mild to moderate amounts of erotic pain. I know many of you will not be pleased with this idea, but I simply must accept the fact that about half of the population finds at least some form of pain erotic. This usually includes relatively minor activities such as mild biting, scratching, spanking, or one partner "mildly" overpowering the other.

The Limits Of Tricks

You know, and I know, that lovemaking cannot be reduced to Tricks. Tricks are to erotic play what spices are to eating. A few carefully chosen ones make the experience more intense and pleasurable. Too many spoil things. Remember, this book is about giving things that are already going well a slight boost.

It's entirely possible to have a wonderful and completely satisfying sex life without knowing any of the Tricks in this book, or any others. Good sex is based on caring about your partner's well being, really wanting to have sex with them (and, of course them really wanting to have sex with you), and observing the responsibilities that go with that. Still, adding a carefully chosen spice now and then can help things along.

Key Point: Your underlying feelings towards the other person, and theirs toward you, greatly affect whether or not a Trick will improve your erotic play. As one lady told me, "If I really like him, then he almost can't do anything wrong. If I really don't like him, then he can't even breathe right."

When A Trick Bombs

Each person has their own unique physical and emotional pattern of erotic responsiveness. Among other things, that means every now and then a Trick that has always worked well before may utterly turn off a new partner. The key phrase for handling this situation is "show compassion for everyone, including yourself."

If what you did really turned your partner off, perhaps even disgusted them, try not to take it too personally. (You wouldn't be human if you didn't take it somewhat personally, but don't buy into that too deeply.) Remember, each person has their own pattern, and you can never completely know what that pattern looks like. Give them a brief apology, if that seems appropriate, then do what you can to move onto something else. There is little to be gained by stopping everything and arguing or debating the point in depth, particularly right then. Save discussions for later.

On the other hand, if your partner starts to do something that really doesn't work for you, please let them know that as soon as you can. "Being polite" in this situation will only allow your displeasure to build to uncontrollable levels. Speak up (diplomatically, please) as soon as possible. Remember, this is almost undoubtedly not willful misconduct on their part. They are probably doing it in an attempt, however misguided, to arouse you. Speak up, but give them the benefit of the doubt – especially if this partner is relatively new.

Find Their Envelope

Tricks don't work well in isolation. Each person has their own erotic response pattern, something I've come to think of as their "envelope." One of your main tasks as a good lover is to find your partner's envelope. This envelope varies considerably from person to person. Among other things, something that is wildly erotic for one person can be grossly unpleasant, even traumatic, for another.

The envelope varies widely from person to person. It also varies over time with the same person. An experience once thought repulsive can become highly attractive, and vice versa. Find their envelope before you try too many Tricks, and remember that the location and content of that envelope change over time.

A Few Don'ts Regarding Tricks (and Other Matters)

1. Don't spend too much time doing Tricks. It's far more important to stay in the here and now with your lover. Do a Trick "every now and then."

2. Don't try to do too many different Tricks in a single session. Again, doing that distances you from your lover.

3. Don't be overly concerned with looking for opportunities to do a Trick. Let such opportunities appear naturally during the course of events. Men seem particularly vulnerable to this pitfall. Thus giving rise to the somewhat bitter saying among many women, "There were three of us in bed. Me, him, and his technique."

4. Never place anything in a woman's vagina if it's recently been in her (or, for that matter, any other person's) anus. Doing so can cause her to get an infection that will require a visit to a doctor and antibiotics to cure. For example, inserting your penis or a dildo into her anus and then into her vagina would be very likely cause such an infection. (A physician once told me that licking a woman's anus and then licking her vagina could cause her to get infected.) Anything used for anal play must first be thoroughly cleaned before it can be used for vaginal play.

5.   Never seal your mouth over a woman's vagina and blow air into it. There are reports of women suffering fatal air embolisms from this practice. Menstruating and pregnant women seem to face a considerably higher than average risk. Such incidents are very, very rare, but they do happen.

6.   Be careful about placing food items in a woman's vagina, especially sugary foods. Many men and women recommended placing various foods in there and then eating them out. (Grapes had something of a cult following.) These foods can upset the natural balance and cause infections, particularly yeast infections. You can do such Tricks if you want, but if you do, then understand that you may have to deal with their effects "the morning after."

Intoxicants

Provided you don't have a substance abuse problem, light use of intoxicants can do a lot to enhance your mood. They can relax tense muscles, take your mind off the worries of the day, and generally calm you down and bring you into the here and now.

I prefer wine. Beer tends to fill up my bladder too quickly (and too often). Harder liquors take me more out of it than I like. I quit using recreational drugs of any kind many years ago.

More than light intoxicant use is asking for trouble. Your judgement becomes dangerously cloudy. Your coordination suffers. You may become too out of it to be sexual at all.

AIDS prevention experts are campaigning against combining sex and intoxicants. They have found that many unsafe sex acts occur when, and – more importantly – only when, the people involved are intoxicated. They compare driving under the influence (D.U.I.) with having sex under the influence (S.U.I.) in terms of danger.

Remember that getting someone too drunk or stoned to understand what is happening and then having sex with them is rape.

As a rule, if you get someone so drunk or stoned that it would be a crime for them to drive, then it would also probably be a crime to have sex with them.

1

Hide And Don't Seek

Because it's important to keep supplies within arm's
reach, and because exactly where that is can vary during
an erotic encounter, one Trickster urges you to keep
your condoms and other supplies in various places
throughout the bedroom – and the rest of the house.

2

Kiss And Make Up

A lady of significant experience has found   that it's
useful for her to carry condoms in her
makeup kit. It's always with her. (She
has also found it useful to
carry them with her tampons.)

3

Hand Job

One Trickster reports repeated success in
arousing lovers by sensuously licking and biting
the palms of their hands.

4

An Open-Faced Tongue Sandwich

Take his cock deep into your mouth. While holding it there, make your tongue flat and soft, then rub its flat surface in circles on the underside of the cock.

5

Cervix Massage

One of my Tricksters reports that she had a lover who drove her wild by inserting his cock deep inside of her, then flicking the end of his cock from side to side over her cervix (with her on her back.)

6

Huff-N-Puff

Give him a literal blow job. Take his cock in your mouth and blow, either with or without a seal created by your lips.

·.·.·
.7.
·.·.·

Throat Tickle

This Trick is best done when the man is on top in missionary position for intercourse. To give your man an extra thrill, try licking him in that cute little hollow spot in his neck just below his Adam's apple.

·.·.·
.8.
·.·.·

Deep Thoughts

Deep throat is a great Trick if you can do it. And if you are fortunate enough to be able to take a man's whole penis into your mouth, try swallowing just at the deepest point of insertion for an extra thrill.

·.·.·
.9.
·.·.·

Two-Lips In The Springtime

Have her lie on her back with her legs spread apart. Sit crosslegged between them, probably with her legs draped over your thighs. Reach down and clasp *both* of her outer labia between your thumb and the side of your forefinger. Grip both the labia together like you would a penis. Now masturbate it like you would a penis. Up and down, side to side, clockwise circles, counterclockwise circles, etc., etc., etc.

10

Ball And Socket

Take just the head of his penis in your mouth,
then pivot your head in clockwise and counterclockwise
circles (don't strain your neck).

11

Up From Beneath

Take their nipple into your mouth, arch your head back
slightly, then run your tongue along the "underside" of
the nipple in clockwise and counterclockwise circles.

12

Squeeze Play

Squeeze his penis tightly, then release. Vary where you
squeeze, how hard, and how long. (Don't grab the penis
and pull straight out, just squeeze.)

·13·

At The Flicks

Place your hand between her legs, palm down and facing toward her toes. Spread her labia apart with your index and third fingers, exposing her clit. Now flick your middle finger down across her clit. Vary pressure and speed as appropriate. Variant: Use your middle finger on the upstroke as well. ♥ Caution: Be careful about the effect your fingernail creates. Make sure it isn't rough or jagged. (Test your fingernails for rough spots by running them along the inside of your forearm.)

·14·

Love Triangle

Put your hand palm down over her breast. Place your thumb and first two fingers in a pyramid over her nipple with the part of your palm just under your index finger resting on her nipple. Squeeze your thumb and fingers together and gently lift her breast. Finish by continuing to lift her breast and letting your fingers slide together off the top of her nipple.

15

The Incredible Disappearing Clitoris

When a woman first becomes aroused, her clitoris becomes larger and more prominent. However, as she approaches orgasm, her clitoris often becomes smaller and withdraws somewhat. Do not take a reduction in clit size as an indication that what you're doing is not working. In fact, just the opposite might be true. And if you stop at that point...

16

Painful Penetration Procedures

If a woman says it hurts when you thrust into her, it may mean (assuming adequate lubrication) that the tip of your penis, or your dildo, is hitting her cervix. Consider the following as a possible remedy. ❤ Under normal, unaroused circumstances, her cervix may protrude into her vaginal canal. However, when she becomes aroused, specific muscles deep in her abdomen may contract. These muscles lift her cervix up and away from the canal, and often even cause a slight hollow to form at the end. ❤ Therefore, if penetration hurts, try waiting until she's more aroused before you enter her.

17

The Remote Control Blow Job

In this Trick, the man being fellated takes the hand of his partner – I suggest using the partner's left hand if they're right handed – and puts their forefinger in his mouth. He then does to his partner's finger what he would like them to do to his cock, and the partner reacts accordingly.

18

Panting Panties

Have the man lie on his back, then hang a soft, sexy panty around his penis, draping down between his legs. Then have intercourse with her on top. The feel of the fabric caressing his testicles and inner thighs can be divine!

19

Conversation Starter

Carry this book in a public place: plane, waiting room, bus, coffee shop. Place it prominently in front of you if necessary, then see who speaks first about it!

20

Take A Breather

Once your gag reflex has been triggered, it's
much easier to trigger it again. Therefore, if you start to
gag during fellatio, switch to some other activity for at
least a few minutes before you try again.

21

Get Wet

Wear sexy and washable lingerie and underwear and
take a shower together – this can be even more erotic
than a wet T-shirt contest.

22

Brush Off

A large soft brush, such as you could buy at an art supply
store or a makeup brush available from almost any drug
store, or a shaving mug brush, can create a thrilling
sensation. It can be used for delightful teasing as well as
– more easily on women than men – to bring your
partner to orgasm. (Note: use it without lube.)   Hold
her vaginal lips open with one hand and use the brush on
the inside of her outer lips, on her inner lips (using both
back and forth and up and down motions), and on her
clit. (Top to bottom on her clit, i.e., hood to tip,
repeatedly, works particularly well.)

23.

Open Says Me

For many women, the sensation of being "opened" carries a heavy erotic charge. With her lying on her back, try holding her legs together as you run your tongue up and down the seam where her thighs meet, teasing the pubic hair and dipping your tongue in the cleft as if your were trying to reach her clit, but you can't quite. ❤ Open her legs after you feel she has suffered enough, but pinch her labia majora shut with your fingers and continue the teasing. Next, spread her majora lips with your hands while you suck the minora lips (together so you keep them shut). Then treat her to the final opening. The tension created can be exquisite and sets the stage for the first full-contact lick of her cunt being almost (note the *almost*) unbearable. Enjoy!

24.

Read *This!*

Large backrest reading pillows are triangle-shaped (viewed from the side). So when you turn them front-side (the side your back would go against) -down they make firm support for someone draped over them... while presenting their backside at an attractively raised angle, ready for whatever fate may await it.

:25:

Dr. Dyke's Leap Of Intelligence

A few drops of water-soluble lubricant placed *inside* a latex glove can make the wearer's fingers more sensitive.

:26:

Hand Job #2

Want to relax and slightly arouse your partner? Give them a nice hand massage, with lots of creamy hand lotion. Consider also massaging their upper arms. (Particularly nice for those who work a lot with their hands.)

:27:

Anal Incentive

If your partner finds it a bit difficult to relax while being penetrated during anal intercourse, try bringing them to orgasm before trying to enter them. The orgasm often helps them relax. Of course, sometimes more than one may be called for.

28

Hear No Evil

It's reliably reported to me that a considerate lady may well be able to increase the intensity of her partner's orgasm during missionary position intercourse by reaching up and snugly plugging her partner's ears with her fingertips (careful with the fingernails).

29

Hair, Hair!

Very lightly pull on their pubic hair, letting your hand slide off. This may also work well on any other hair on their body.

30

Comb As You Are

Luxuriously comb their pubic hair. Do it very deliberately and slowly.

31

Eau D'You

Ladies, dab a little of your vaginal juices behind your ears, on your wrists – wherever you'd normally wear perfume.

32

Head Games

Ladies, try dry humping the crown of his head, especially if he's nearly or completely bald. The woman who told me of this Trick said that it gave her an incredible feeling of "I'm fucking his brain!"

33

Forearmed Is Foreplay

Hold his cock in one hand and rub it with the inside of your forearm. The extra-smooth sensation can feel wonderful. (This can work on nipples, too.)

34

Shake Her Booby

Grab her nipple(s) between forefinger and thumb and shake. (Read the spanking section before doing this Trick.)

.35.

Warm Hands, Warm Heart

Place your (unlubricated) hands palm to palm together in front of you so your fingers are pointing away from you, then rub them vigorously together in a front-to-back motion. The friction thus created warms your hands and can make receiving your touch extra pleasurable. To build this, rub them together for a full minute.

.36.

Peek-A-Boo

If you have long hair, veil yourself during fellatio and only occasionally let him see his cock in your mouth.

.37.

The Boy Scout Motto: Be Prepared!

If you, fella, don't want to be too horny on a date, masturbate to orgasm just before you go out for the evening.

38
Coming Right Up!

It's often very useful and helpful to signal to your partner, verbally or otherwise, that you are about to come, especially when you are receiving fellatio.

39
Taste Test

Several Tricksters report that the taste of a man's cock often noticeably changes just before he comes.

40
Saturday Night Fever

This Trick is best done while wearing a well-lubricated latex glove on each hand. Put one index finger in her vagina and the other in her anus. Alternate strokes with them, or put them in at the same time. Remember that once something has been in her (or any other person's) anus, it should not be inserted into her vagina until it has been *very* thoroughly cleaned.

·····
41
·····

A Genderous Impulse

Try role reversal on gender names: She calls him names
such as "bitch," he calls her names such as "sir."

·····
42
·····

Crew Cut Special

Several Tricksters report that it feels great to have their
genitals brushed with short head hair.

·····
43
·····

Round And Round We Go

Grab his penis at its base with one hand, then
use the sides of the forefinger of your other hand
to circle the corona.

·····
44
·····

Pull Toy

Grab her labia and pull, gently but firmly, straight down
towards her feet. This Trick will work whether you hold
both labia in one hand, or one in each hand. Then, if you
like, vibrate or shake your hand or hands.

··· 45 ···
Knuckle Sandwich

A lady Trickster reports that it feels wonderful
when her partner rolls the knuckles of their
well-lubricated fist against her pussy.

··· 46 ···
Giddyap!

Ladies, playing "horsey" by kneeling astride your
partner's well-lubricated thigh can be hot.

··· 47 ···
Menstrual Magic

Many people feel somewhat reluctant to perform
cunnilingus on a woman during her period. Tricksters
report that performing cunnilingus through silk panties
(while she has a tampon in place) can be a "double-win"
approach. Please note that the silk is quite permeable
and thus should not be considered a safer sex device.

48

Burn, Baby, Burn

Plastic wrap applied to the inner thighs, possibly
with lubricant underneath, just prior to cunnilingus,
helps prevent whisker burn.

49

A Close Shave

So does a fresh shave just before performing cunnilingus.

50

The Napes Have It

Lightly brush the back of their neck in a down-to-up
direction, against the grain.

51

Knock, Knock, Come In

It's been reported that fellatio can often be
enhanced by tapping the shaft of the penis while your
mouth works on its head.

52

Just A Pinch For Seasoning

Many a person's orgasm can be enhanced by pinching their labia or the skin of the scrotum (not the actual testicles) as they come. The welcome degree of pressure can range from very light to distinctly strong. Experiment. Communicate. Explore.

53

Bend-N-Stretch

Place the heel of the palm of your hand on her mons (pubic mound) and push up toward her stomach. This creates a stretching sensation and can expose her clit. Then stimulate her manually or orally.

54

"Glad" Wrap

Apply baby powder or oil to the penis, then "buff" it in a back-and-forth motion with plastic wrap.

55

Baggie Pants

Place a substantial squirt of lube in a plastic sandwich bag, then place it over his cock and masturbate him with it.

56

The Pits Aren't The Pits

The armpit is a neglected erogenous zone. It's a seldom-touched area, and thus often very sensitive.

57

As Below, So Above

I mentioned in the first "Tricks" book that the backs of the knees are often a very sensitive, erotic area. Since then, it's been reported to me that the insides of the elbows can also be very sensitive.

58

Play Her Like A Violin

Rub a longish hair back and forth across her clit like a violin string.

59

Chinese Water Torture

Drip lukewarm water slowly on her clit. Try a drip rate of about one drop per second for starters. Adjust rate and temperature as needed.

:60:
Lick, Don't Swallow

Let's say you are performing fellatio and your partner
begins to have an orgasm. You don't want to
swallow his semen, and yet you also want to give him a
very pleasurable orgasm. Try using the tip of your
tongue to briskly lick along the underside of his penis,
just at the junction of the shaft and the head. Continue
doing this for nearly a minute. ❤ He should have a very
pleasant orgasm (trust me on this) and yet very little of
his semen should get into your mouth.
This technique can sometimes provide a very acceptable
compromise between swallowing his semen and pulling
your mouth away entirely.

:61:
Toothbrush Trick I

Use a toothbrush to slightly abrade your
partner's nipples. This makes them more
sensitive to strokes, etc.

:62:
Toothbrush Trick II

Run the toothbrush, bristle side down, along the crease
where the thigh meets the body, running from back to
front and front to back.

.63.

Toothbrush Trick III

Use the bristles to lightly scratch the genitals, inner thighs, etc. As one lady put it, "When the bristles are used just right on my already-lubricated clit, it feels like good cunnilingus."

.64.

Toothbrush Trick IV

Use the back of the toothbrush to masturbate her clitoris and otherwise caress her outer genitals.

.65.

Toothbrush Trick V

Use the back of the toothbrush to spank the genitals and inner thighs. Start with very light spanks, and establish a safeword ahead of time. Be especially careful when spanking his testicles. (Read the "Spanking Tricks" section before attempting this Trick.)

∙∙∙∙∙
.66.
∙∙∙∙∙

Toothbrush Trick VI

The gum massager on the base of the toothbrush opens up a whole new world of possibilities. If it feels too sharp, spend some time before you use the toothbrush bending and softening the tip until it's just right.

∙∙∙∙∙
.67.
∙∙∙∙∙

Toothbrush Trick VII

Toothbrush safety precautions: ❤ Use a toothbrush *only* when you have enough light to see what you are doing. ❤ A soft or medium stiffness toothbrush is likely to give more erotic sensations than a firm one. ❤ *Do not* insert the toothbrush. Doing so can be terribly dangerous. Use a toothbrush only on external surfaces. ❤ Clean the toothbrush thoroughly before using it on anybody else. ❤ Better yet, use a given toothbrush only on one particular person. Toothbrushes are cheap, so buy several. ❤ Using the toothbrush to abrade or spank will remove outer layers of skin. This will, among other things, make the skin much more sensitive to menthol Tricks (see "Menthol Tricks" in the first "Tricks" book), so be careful. A quantity of menthol that is easily tolerated on "untoothbrushed" skin can be too painful on "toothbrushed" skin.

·68·
Give Them A Hand

Have your lover take one of your hands in both of theirs, and instruct them to touch their body with it. Let them touch and "wash" their body with your hand. This can work particularly well when you are touching them for the first time.

·69·
Brushing Up

Tricksters report that it can feel wonderful to gently use a hairbrush on their lover's genital area. A separate hairbrush can be used on the anal area, if you like.

·70·
Let's Spoon

Take an ordinary teaspoon, or perhaps several, and put them in the refrigerator (*not* the freezer!), then bring them out and run them one at time over your lover's body. Perhaps you can even insert the spoon into her vagina. (Not too deeply, just the bowl of the spoon.) ❤ It's possible to enhance this Trick by keeping a bowl of ice water that has several spoons in it by the bed. One can be in use while the others are chilling.

71

Under The Hood

Some Tricksters have reported to me, *very* emphatically, that it's possible to make cunnilingus much more intense for some women by gently pulling back the clitoral hood to expose the tissue normally covered by it, and then licking there.

72

Thumb Strum

Sit between his legs and grasp his cock firmly in both hands, with your fingers between his cock and stomach and your thumbnails facing toward the ceiling. Run the ball of each thumb in turn up the underside of his penis, from the root toward the head, lifting the thumb away from the penis when it reaches the head. Repeat, alternating thumbs, smoothly and rapidly. This masturbation stroke gives him very intense stimulation to the sensitive underside of the head of his penis.

73

A Hairy Story

If you have long hair, try placing some of it between your hand and your lover's penis while you masturbate him.

·74·
Finger-Lickin' Good

Cunnilingus can often be enhanced by moving two fingers in and out of her vagina while you lick her clitoris. This in and out motion can often be enhanced by twisting your fingers as you move them in and out.

·75·
There's A Point To All This

The spot on the underside of the penis, just below the notch in the head, is often exceptionally receptive to being licked and stroked. Tantra practitioners sometimes refer to this location as Osho's Point, and make good use of it.

·76·
Fuck 'Em If They Can't Take A Joke

The following Trick is a little bit sneaky, but it can be great fun. While your lover has your cock in their mouth, crack a joke or otherwise do something to make them laugh. The resulting sensation can feel marvelous, and your lover probably won't mind too much.

:77:

Give 'Em A Lift

This Trick can greatly enhance doggie-style intercourse.
Take a thick bathrobe sash, or similar type of material,
preferably at least six feet long. Fold it in half, and
perhaps knot the two ends together. The person in the
rear then loops the sash around their partner's hips and
grabs the ends that come out from either side. (It may
work better if the knot protrudes from one of the sides.)
Grab the two "handles" thus created, and enjoy.

:78:

I-i-i-n-n-n A-a-n-n-d O-o-o-u-u-t-t-t

As a refreshing change from the usual flopping and
hammering away of traditional intercourse, the man can
try a series of *very slow* insertions and withdrawals of his
penis, perhaps taking five to ten seconds, perhaps even
longer, to enter or withdraw.

.79.

Battering Ram

This is a very simple Trick, and yet it can be extremely powerful. It is probably done best in the "doggie-style" position for intercourse. The man withdraws his penis almost all the way, pauses for a second, then suddenly "rams" forward with considerable force, all the way in. The process can, if desired, be repeated any number of times. (He should make sure he is properly lined up or he can cause significant injury to either himself or his partner.) Obviously, this Trick should probably be reserved for a time when intercourse has already been underway for a while, not done right at the beginning. ♥ Footnote: This type of thrust can often be combined with the extremely slow withdrawal described in Trick 78, to excellent effect. ♥ Second Footnote: If she is prone to bladder infections, this Trick could possibly create problems.

·····
80
·····

Bump-N-Grind

This Trick often works very well during missionary-position intercourse. It's a bit subtle, so pay close attention. While the man is on top, he slightly shifts his body so that he is a bit "higher" upon her body than he usually is. (Her nose will be just a bit lower than normal.) He is then in a position to "grind" his pubic bone against hers. Properly done, this technique can significantly increase the amount of clitoral stimulation she receives.

·····
81
·····

Lube Tube

In a remarkable example of extremely poor planning, many excellent lubricants intended for use during sex come in bottles that are hard to open if your hands are slippery. This is particularly true of bottles that must be unscrewed or pulled to open. Tricksters respond to this problem by pouring the lubricant in question into small bottles that have flip-up spouts.

82.

Warm Thoughts

Relaxed nudity requires warmth. Usually at least 75 degrees, sometimes more. A room thermometer kept in a discreet place in your bedroom can help make sure you provide a "user friendly" environment.

83.

Straw Boss

Want to give *her* a blow job? Use a swizzle stick, or some other very narrow type of straw, to blow air on her clit.

84.

YES!!!

When you are doing something to your lover, it can be wonderful to hear the word "yes" in reply. There can be dozens of different ways to say "yes" in response to your lover's attentions. Try them. Try saying "yes" in many, many different ways.

·85·

Cunni-Fingus

To build your lady's anticipation for a subsequent sexual encounter, try this: At the movies or a restaurant, take her hand in one of yours. Gently spread apart her index finger and middle finger and hold them about an inch apart, supporting her hand with yours. Moisten the index finger of your other hand. Then, with your moistened finger, stroke the inner side of her index finger in tiny light feather strokes, working your way toward the web between the fingers. Then do the same to the inside of her middle finger. End by placing your index fingertip directly over the web between the two fingers and gently stroking upwards about a quarter of an inch with the same light feather touch. The symbolism, if not the sensation, will drive her crazy.

·86·

A Palatable Suggestion

Male Tricksters report that if they can feel the head of their cock on the roof of their partner's mouth, then it *really* feels like it's in their partner's mouth.

87

Nota Bene

When expecting a lover, pin a note to the front door (folded over with their name on the outside) and inside have a message such as "Hey big guy, I've been waiting for you!" or some other "hot" message. (See Trick #93.)

88

Playing Nurse

Take just a small amount of his soft cock in your mouth and nurse on it, just like a baby would nurse on a bottle or nipple.

89

You Beast, You

If you want to add a touch of primordial energy to your lovemaking, and that can be a very powerful touch indeed, try making only animal noises while you have sex.

·90·

Getting Wet And Staying Wet

I have a few "Underwater Tricksters" who advise me that you can use silicon lubricant, available in scuba stores, for having sex in the water. (If you've ever tried to have sex in the water, as I have, you probably learned that our natural lubricants get washed away very quickly.) My Tricksters advise me that this silicon lubricant works very well for keeping things adequately slippery for in-water sex, but wears off in *a day or two*, so be advised on that point. I'm also advised that it is condom-compatible.

·91·

Taking A Chance On Love

Many, many Tricksters have suggested a variant on the following: Put the numbers of various Tricks in a bowl and draw one. Then do that Trick. Repeat. The more Trick numbers in the bowl, the more mutually satisfying this Trick is to all concerned.

92.

Hooker's Trick #6: "I Don't Do That"

Sex work can be a very stressful occupation. Smart sex workers know that they need to take a number of measures to take care of themselves. One such self-care measure is to have a clear sense of their own limits and boundaries, and to gently (at least at first) but firmly insist that clients respect those limits. ♥ When a client asks them to do something that is beyond their limits, and *many* clients will test to see if the stated limits are in fact the actual limits, workers often find it best to immediately reply, in a steady yet not hostile voice, "I'm sorry, but I don't do that." ♥ Because it's bad business to turn the customer down flat and then leave an awkward silence, many workers will then suggest the closest acceptable alternative, but if the request comes up again, or another unacceptable request is made, their reply is once again a steady "I'm sorry, but I don't do that." A counter-proposal is then again made. ♥ It's rare that a third request is made, but if it is, the worker immediately returns once again to a considerate, yet firm, "I'm sorry, but I don't do that."

·····
·93·
·····

String Them Along

Tied into Trick 87, have a note saying "follow the string."
Then, as they follow the string, they will find pieces of
clothing seductively thrown along the way until they
finally reach you reclining on the bed appropriately "gift
wrapped." The string could be routed via the
refrigerator, with a note on the fridge saying "Bring
champagne" (or sparkling cider, if you prefer) "and two
glasses from the refrigerator."

·····
·94·
·····

Nature Loves A Vacuum

If your male lover gets off on having his cock
sucked, try using your mouth to make a seal around it
and *really* creating a vacuum for him to enjoy.
Slight movements of your head can increase the
sensations associated with this.

·····
·95·
·····

Toe To Toe

Sit facing each other in a tub of comfortably warm water
and masturbate her with your toes. To add even more
spice, suck her toes at the same time.

96

"Fist Fucking"

Grasp the penis just below its head in a firm but not tight fist. Take the head of the penis, above your fist, in your mouth. He can then thrust his penis through your fist into your mouth, creating the desired friction with his own motion.

97

Come Across The Ridge

When you are doing either manual or oral stimulation of your male partner and you want him to come, make sure your strokes of his penis go all the way up the shaft and slip over the ridge of the penis. The area on the lower edge of this ridge (the frenulum) is where the nerve endings live that result most easily in orgasm.

In many men, you have to stimulate this area to produce an orgasm — or *avoid* stimulating this area for him to not have one.

98

Be Prepared #2

If you want to increase the volume of your ejaculate,
try masturbating before you have a date with your love
and stopping a minute or so before you come.
(Don't try to wait until the absolute last second or you
might wait a bit too long.)

99

Etc., Etc., Etc.

Many Tricksters have reported to me that
constant repetition of the same tongue stroke
works well if you are performing cunnilingus and want
her to come. If you want to make her come, find a
stroke that she likes and keep repeating it. If you want to
prolong things, vary your strokes.

100

Enter By The Side Or Rear

In keeping with the theme that seldom-touched
parts of the body are often erogenous zones, let me
report that the sides and the rear wall of the
scrotum is often wonderfully sensitive to light stroking
by fingers or a tongue.

101

What's Your Hurry?

It has been reported to me by many different Tricksters that cunnilingus can be greatly improved by not going directly for her clitoris. Take your time, explore.

102

O, My Goodness!

Building, as it were, on the Trick above, it's also reported that exuberantly circling her clit with your tongue can produce a wonderful effect.

103

Watering Can

Water-based lubricants are seeing much wider use than they previously did. (They're compatible with condom usage, whereas oil-based lubricants can dissolve a condom.) Unfortunately, water-based lubricants "dry out" much more quickly that oil-based lubes do. Tricksters thus often keep a small, fliptop bottle of water close to their small, fliptop bottle of lube. (See Trick #81.) One *very* useful way to accomplish this is to tape or glue the two bottles together. This is an almost optimally handy arrangement.

104

Mountain Range

The Trick "Climbing the Mountain" (which, by the way, I invented) was described in the first "Tricks" book. This is an extremely powerful technique for masturbating a man. To give a quick summary of how it's done, you give his penis one quick stroke, then sensually caress it for about ten seconds, this is followed by two quick strokes, and another ten seconds of caresses, then three strokes and ten seconds of caresses, and then four strokes... you get the idea. ♥ Extremely simple, yet extremely powerful variants of this Trick involve applying exactly the same principle to fellatio, cunnilingus, masturbating a woman, or intercourse.

105

Soft Fur

Many a considerate male Trickster applies a good-smelling hair conditioner to his beard before performing cunnilingus. (Leave it on the beard for at least a few minutes; the softness it creates can last for hours.) Doing so can dramatically reduce the amount of "whisker burn" his lady love must endure.

106

Bull's-Eyes Don't Always Win

Lady Tricksters ask me to remind my readers that there's more to a breast than just its nipple. Please spend time paying attention to some of the rest of that lovely skin.

107

Rub-A-Dub-Dub

Some of my more well-travelled Tricksters, particularly those who have spent a bit of time in the Far East (while perhaps on the government payroll) report that, when used with *very* soapy water, it is possible to use the penis, vaginal area, and breasts as excellent massage tools. I gather it is possible to visit establishments where this Trick is something of a house specialty.

108

Third Eye Bliss

The area just between and above the eyes, the "third eye" area, is often very receptive to being stroked, massaged, and so forth.

109

Jet Set

A very popular Trick, suggested by many, is the use of a steady jet of water on the woman's vaginal/clitoral area. While the streams coming into hot tubs and swimming pools are popular, the handpieces that can be attached to shower heads seem to be the most often recommended.

Of course, great fun can be had experimenting with variations on the water's temperature and pressure, and with the various spray pattern settings on the handpiece.

110

Speechless

Sometimes using words to communicate your wants to your lover does not enhance the mood. If nonverbal communication seems more appropriate, try this technique taught by many sex therapists. Take their hand (or hands) or their head gently in your own hands, and guide it to where you want it to go.

•••••
111
•••••

Smart Mouth

In these somewhat risky times, using a condom is often an extremely smart thing to do. Unfortunately, many men aren't all that happy about being asked to wear one. One method of talking him into wearing one that has a reasonably good chance of success it to offer to put it on him by using your mouth. ♥ Here are a few tips. (1) Practice. A few "dry runs" on a dildo, vibrator, or a willing "practice dummy" will help greatly.
(2) The lubricant may not taste all that great. Consider buying unlubricated condoms, or try "dry runs" using various brands until you find one whose taste you find acceptable. (3) Press the air out of the condom's tip with your tongue. This will help reduce the odds of it breaking. (4) To put the condom on a soft cock, it is often useful to position it in your mouth and then suck his penis up into it.

•••••
112
•••••

Cape of Good Hope

One of the many Tricks contributed by "The Retired Courtesan" is as follows: "I have more than once arrived at a man's house dressed in a big, ankle-length cape. Then I invite him to open (or unzip) the cape and underneath I am either naked or wearing something very seductive."

113

Hooker's Trick #7

In the first "Tricks" book, and in this one, I presented several "Hooker's Tricks," i.e. techniques often taught by one sex worker to another for use on clients. I did a few consultations with sex workers in the process of preparing this book, and one of them shared the following "Rules of The Trade" with me. ❤ Always get paid in advance. (This is their big Rule Number One.) ❤ Never let them tie you up. ❤ Never permit emotional involvement to develop, either of them towards you or, especially, of you towards them.

114

Love That Leather!

A lady of considerable and varied experience reports that wearing light leather gloves can often add a delicious touch.

115
Leg Lift

Sit between your partner's legs as they lie on their back.
Bring your partner close to orgasm, or have them bring
themselves close to orgasm. Just as they begin to come,
lift their legs strongly toward the ceiling. The blood rush
to the genital area, plus the stretching of the muscles in
the legs, may greatly enhance their orgasm.

116
Icy Hot

A Trickster writes, "On hot days my wife is often very
flushed and overheated after having an orgasm. As a
surprise, I'll go down on her with an ice cube in my
teeth. The effect of the other fluids mixing with the
rapidly melting ice creates a hot and cold swirl. She
usually has another orgasm from this treatment if it's
done soon enough. Her reaction is usually to
flinch away from the cold at first, then press into it. I
don't keep the ice in constant contact, but use it
occasionally whenever that feels right."

117

"Did You Come?"

I have learned that it's not always the greatest idea in the world to ask a partner, particularly a new partner, that question immediately after sex. For one thing, how important coming was to them can vary, both in terms of the partner and of their desires at the time. Sometimes it's terribly important; sometimes it's no big deal either way; sometimes they may not have wanted to come (and sometimes they don't know whether they came or not). ❤ Some partners may really want you to do something about it if they haven't come, and others would rather let things wind down. If coming is important to them, your options regarding what to do about it may be more limited at that point than they were before. (Many people are happy to masturbate themselves while you hold and caress them; others would prefer that you participate more directly.) ❤ It is often difficult, especially with a new female partner, to tell whether or not she has come. Ladies, want to do your new lover a favor? If you come, tell them so. This is almost never unwelcome news, and hearing it can be a great relief. ❤ (Footnote: A next-day discussion regarding how things went, including but not limited to that particular topic, is often a good idea.)

118
Tummy Trick

Here's a Trick that can increase the pleasure a
woman feels while you masturbate her. Insert
some fingers, usually two, into her vagina. While
that hand is pleasuring her, take the palm of your other
hand, place it on her abdomen just above her pubic
bone, and press down – perhaps rather firmly. The
results can be impressive.

119
Whisker Off

The problems relating to "whisker burn" are mentioned
above (see Tricks #48 and #49). However, the *intentional,
focused* application of facial hair – ranging from stubble to
an actual beard – to the genitals and other body parts of
your partner can create powerful effects.

120
Nota Bene #2

It's fun to wake up and find love notes pinned or taped all
over the bedroom, or perhaps even the whole house,
saying how wonderful you are.

121

Nota Bene #3

As a variant of Trick 120, I used to have a "long-distance" relationship with one of my lovers. She could only visit me every few months or so. At the end of her visit, when it was time to drive her to the airport, she would arrange it so that she would be the last person to leave the house. When I returned to the house, there would be notes to me scattered about – some in plain sight, some hidden. Finding them over the next few hours, and finding a few a day or so later, was great fun.

122

Collar Of Kisses

Kiss them on the neck. Do it very sensuously. Then move just slightly to the side and kiss them again on their neck. Continue. Create a "collar of kisses" around their neck. Doing so can transport both of you into another world.

123

It's Saliva!

A recent report in a scientific journal reported that exposing the HIV virus to saliva very substantially reduced its infectivity. Saliva does not appear to kill the virus, but it does seem to damage it in such a way that the virus becomes *much* less able to infect a host cell. This is perhaps due to the action of enzymes in saliva on the outer coat of the virus. ♥ The above being true, if you are using a lubricant and it begins to "dry out," consider moistening it with your saliva as an additional option to using more lube or more water. This extra bit of protection could be useful.

124

Scrotum Stretch

Gently grip his scrotum and slowly pull downwards, towards his feet. This can be done either by grasping the skin at the bottom of the scrotum or by making a circle with your thumb and forefinger at the top of the scrotum. Be sure to increase the strength of your pull very slowly and pay close attention to how he is reacting. There is such a thing as too little pressure (no big deal), too much pressure (painful, perhaps even damaging), and "just right" pressure (Ohhhhh, yesssss).

125

The Moist Years

As women age, the amount of vaginal lubrication they produce when aroused may decline, often to a not-enough level. A visit to the local pharmacy can help with this problem. They usually stock simple glycerin vaginal suppositories that can provide adequate lubrication. Because these suppositories contain no birth control chemicals or other potentially harsh agents, there are very few reports of any problem with them, and many, many satisfied users. Some women prefer different brands, so experiment. ♥ If none of the over-the-counter brands are satisfactory, see your doctor. Prescription estrogen creams may help.

Spanking Tricks - And A Few Related Others

As some of you know, after publishing the first "Tricks" book I published a book called "SM 101: A Realistic Introduction." This very large book – nearly 250 pages and over 125,000 words in length – is a comprehensive guide to that particular type of very exciting (*and* very risky) consensual erotic play.

In the first "Tricks" book, I faced something of a dilemma in that the criteria for a Trick was that it had to be something which could be done with just the bodies of the people involved or with an item likely to be found in the average household, and much SM play can be done exactly that way. Therefore, activities such as spanking technically qualified. Nevertheless, I decided to pass on such activities for that particular book. (I did, admittedly somewhat arbitrarily, decide that "menthol Tricks" were acceptable, and have to date received no negative feedback regarding that decision.)

Now, given that my SM book is readily available, and given that spanking is much more widely known as a form of erotic play than it was even a few years ago (Thank you, Madonna!), and given that spanking – and a few related activities – do meet the "Tricks" criteria, I decided to include them in this book – along with a *very* generous helping of warnings, safety tips, and advisories.

A Serious Caution

If your play in this area moves beyond using anything outside of just your bodies, it's terribly important – perhaps quite literally of life and death importance – to get proper instruction and education first.

Don't try to tie each other up with any sort of clothesline or other material, or engage in any sort of erotic play involving physical equipment, *particularly* formal SM gear such as handcuffs, riding crops, clamps, and so forth, without first receiving instruction in their proper and safe use.

I want to caution you specifically about bondage. It may appear that bondage is one of the least dangerous aspects of SM play, yet it is actually one of the most dangerous. Bondage is not usually highly dangerous in and of itself, but rather because of how it "sets the stage" for what might happen next. Being alone and tied up with a drunken, stoned, crazy, psychopathic, or malicious person is a horror to contemplate and – as I once found out – even worse to experience.

What's more, being alone and tied up with a well-meaning but non-comprehending person is not all that great. (I know of some rather serious, and absolutely genuine, problems that have taken place when the uninformed dominant misunderstood what the submissive "really" wanted to happen, even though the submissive was honestly pleading for the activity to be stopped and for their partner to untie them.) Bondage can often be *much* more dangerous than it appears to be. Remember that.

I consider SM to be the riskiest form of sex. Its risk level compares to that of sports activities such as skydiving, white water rafting, or auto racing. You wouldn't dream (I hope!) of trying those activities without first receiving proper instruction. It's very important that you take the same approach to using SM equipment. For more information, please refer to the section in this book called "Some Warnings About SM."

How Likely Is It That A Partner Will Find It Erotic To Spank Or Be Spanked?

From what I have been able to gather, about one person in three will find the whole idea a complete turn-off and want nothing to do with it. There is usually little that can be done about their attitude other than accept it as gracefully as you can. You might talk with them about the nature of their concerns, and offer them a very non-threatening opportunity to try it, but don't push. A "hard sell" in this situation is likely to accomplish little except to waste your time and annoy them – or worse.

The second person in this group of three is likely to be willing to try spanking, in one role or the other, but will discover that it arouses few or no feelings in them – either positive or negative. This person may continue to be involved in spanking, usually to a limited degree, if doing so pleases their lover, but it doesn't do much for them – and they frequently come to resent the whole thing after a while.

The third person in this group of three may discover that giving and/or receiving a spanking (or some other form of SM, and I definitely consider spanking a form of SM) does arouse them.

In summary, you can estimate that only about *one person in six*, if chosen at random, will be genuinely receptive to being spanked. Looked at another way, five people out of six will *not* be interested – although one of them might be interested in spanking *you*. (Some people who enjoy spanking enjoy both roles, by the way.)

How Can Spanking Be Erotic?

Nobody is sure of the reasons why spanking arouses some people (a very few even to the point of orgasm) and undoubtedly the reasons for this arousal vary from person to person. Some people speculate that the nerves running to and from the buttocks are very close to the nerves that run to and from the genitals and may be, in some as yet undiscovered manner, more closely linked in some people than in others. (This linkage could exist either in the peripheral nerves and/ or within the brain itself, possibly the limbic area.) Thus strong stimulation in the buttocks somehow "echoes" to the genitals.

(A similar mechanism has been postulated regarding the genitals and the feet, thus potentially explaining at least part of why some people find feet so fascinating and wonderful.)

Please Note Well: There is no objective, scientific evidence to support the assertion that an interest in spanking, or in any other form of consensual, caring SM play, is in and of itself a sign of any type of mental illness or disorder.

Setting the Stage for Spanking and Related Tricks

A.   Read this section and the section "Some Warnings About SM" several times. It would also be an excellent idea – and a caring, responsible act on your part – to show these sections to your proposed spanking partner. Never "surprise" a partner with either a spanking or a request for a spanking.

B.   Avoid spanking or being spanked if either person is intoxicated, tired, upset, or otherwise not at their best.

C.   Establish an agreed-upon "safe word" before beginning. (Also see the "two squeezes" section below.) Note well: If there is *any* doubt in your mind as to whether or not the person receiving (or giving) the spanking is feeling all right about it, stop and check in with them. Staying connected is essential.

General Pointers On Giving or Receiving a Spanking

Spankings are often given with the receiver lying face-down on a comfortable surface (massage tables can be excellent) or kneeling on a carpeted floor with their body across something, such as a bed, that allows them to rest the weight of their torso and head. It is very useful to put the receiver in a position where they can relax as much as possible, especially if they are new at this. It's especially important to avoid positions stressful to the receiver's back and/or neck.

One classic spanking form is the over-the-knee position. A position that can allow the receiver to relax is for the spanker to sit on the side of the bed and for the receiver to stretch out across their lap.

For safety's sake, the receiver's hands should be positioned well away from their buttocks, preferably at or above their waist, and should stay there throughout the spanking. (Many people, even those quite willing to be spanked, will reflexively swing their hands down to cover their buttocks. This can injure either or both parties.)

One possibility is to have the receiver rest their forehead on their forearms or hands. They can also perhaps rest their hands on the back of their head, or place them out to the side in a sort of "T-position." If an appropriate pillow is available, they can place their hands and forearms across their abdomen while the pillow supports their chest. If a massage table is being used, an "arm cradle" can be useful. The position should be as comfortable and strain-free as possible.

This position can also serve as something of a safety device. If the receiver keeps their hands in place, it can show that they are willing (and, hopefully, eager) to have the spanking continue. However, if they "break position," the spanking should be stopped until the receiver returns to their previous position. (Both parties should agree on this before the spanking begins.)

The spanker should remove any rings, watches, bracelets, and so forth that might be damaged, or might cause injury by coming into contact with the receiver's body.

The spanker should take a moment to locate the receiver's tailbone. It's usually felt at the junction of the lower back and the buttock cheeks. A hard blow here could dislocate or even fracture the tailbone, so stay away from this particular area.

The spanking is usually done with the fingers of the hand together and slightly cupped. The spank itself often feels better when delivered in a slightly "upward" direction.

Where To Spank, And Where Not To

It's useful to visualize each buttock as being divided into four quadrants – inner and outer, lower and upper. The lower, inner quadrant is often the place where the spank feels best. (It's known in many SM circles as "the sweet spot.") The upper, outer quadrant is often the least erotic, but that can vary from person to person.

The backs of the thighs, and the inner thighs, can also be spanked. The sensation feels distinctly different here, and people vary considerably in whether or not they enjoy it.

Be very careful to refrain from spanking a man's testicles. This can be avoided by only giving spankings when there is enough light to clearly see where they are, by covering his testicles with one of your hands while you spank with the other, or by having him cover his testicles with his own hands. You could also try having him use his hand to bring his testicles forward and then closing his legs together, thus keeping them relatively safe in front of this body.

Repeated spanks in the same place (such as the same quadrant of the buttock) can rapidly become unerotic. Vary where you spank. As a rule, don't spank more than twice in a row in any one particular quadrant, particularly if you aren't too familiar with how this partner reacts.

How Long Should the Spanking Last?

Don't continue the spanking too long. Again, this is especially important if this partner is new either to you or to spanking (or, especially, both). Some people like only the briefest of spankings. Others (maybe one person in a hundred) absolutely love to receive a strong spanking that lasts for a very long time. As a rule for beginners, a first spanking that lasts for a total of about five minutes should be more than fine. Longer spankings can be arranged for future get-togethers. Remember that, as is true with almost all other aspects of SM play, you almost never get into serious trouble by going too slowly.

Communication After the Spanking Session

It's very important for both parties to talk afterwards about what worked and what didn't work for them regarding the spanking. Immediately after the spanking session is often not that great a time for this discussion, because either or both parties may have emotional or physical reactions that have made them somewhat off balance or "spacey." Discussing the spanking the next day often works very well. It's very important that this conversation take place *well in advance* of a second spanking.

And now, the spanking Tricks themselves.

Spanking Trick 1

"Now"

Raise your slightly cupped hand about twelve inches above the receiver's buttocks and hold it there. Tell them you will give them one light spank after – and only after – they say the word "now." When you hear the "now," bring your hand down on one of their buttocks. Use just slightly more force than your hand would generate if it were to fall on their buttocks. When (and if) the receiver says another "now," bring your hand down with the same force upon their other buttock. Continue this alternating pattern. ♥ "Now" should apply to only a single spank at first. As you gain more experience and knowledge, it can be applied to previously agreed-upon groups of two, four, six, or more. ♥ This approach to spanking is very useful in helping the receiver retain their emotional balance and a sense of control over what is happening. "Now" helps ensure that their spanking experience will be positive, enjoyable, and not overwhelmingly intense.

Spanking Trick 2

"One To Ten"

Raise your hand about twelve inches above the receiver's buttocks and let it drop. Tell the receiver that the stroke they just received had a strength of three. A "two" is about half that forceful, and a "one" is little more than a very light touch. The strength of the spanks can go all the way up to "ten" with each spank above three being about 25% stronger than the previous number. ♥ Tell the receiver that when they call out a number, it will indicate both the strength of the spank they are willing to receive *and* that they are willing to receive it. Tell the receiver that this number can *both* increase and decrease. ♥ Like the "Now" Trick, this Trick is very useful in helping the receiver, particularly a novice, retain their emotional balance. They are thus much more likely to open up to and enjoy the experience.

Spanking Trick 3

Experience Spanking from Both Ends

Even if you love to receive a spanking but hate to give one (or vice versa), you'll learn many valuable lessons from "switching roles" occasionally. Depending on what's appropriate, this switching can be done either with your regular partner or with another person.

Spanking Trick 4

Rub After Spanking

One excellent way to convert a painful spank into an erotic sensation is to massage the skin immediately after delivering the stroke. Bring the spank down, still your hand for about one to two seconds, then massage the freshly spanked area using moderate-to-slightly-heavy pressure. Have someone do this to you and you'll understand.

Spanking Trick 5

Keep "Reality" Out of It

Spanking fans often role-play situations (naughty pupil and teacher, disobedient child and baby sitter, etc.) to act out spanking fantasies. These scenarios often involve someone getting "punished" for some supposed "misconduct." All well and good. ♥ However, it's *very* important to keep real world situations out of spanking games. Spanking someone because they forgot to pay the phone bill, left the lights on, or did something similar that you really didn't like, can be a recipe for disaster. Spanking games are consensual, erotic, fantasy play, not a place to settle scores or grudges. Those get handled in "straight time," not in the bedroom.

Spanking Trick 6

Harder Is Not Necessarily Better

People who enjoy giving and/or receiving spankings vary
tremendously in how hard they want their spankings to be,
and how often they want to give or receive one. It's important
for each individual to find out what works best specifically for
them. Just remember: Harder is not necessarily better. More
painful is not necessarily better. Longer is not necessarily better.
More often is not necessarily better.

Spanking Trick 7

Tips On Receiving a Spanking

Some people prefer to receive their spanking lying
face down. Others prefer to be bent over at the waist.
Some prefer the standing erect position. Each has its own
unique aspects. Experiment.

Spanking Trick 8

More Tips On Receiving a Spanking

Breathe. Try not to let your breathing constrict.
Deliberately take a deep breath and try to relax on the exhale.
Also, experiment with buttock tension. Experience how the
spanking feels when your buttocks muscles are very tense, then
very loose, then somewhere in the middle.

Spanking Trick 9

Two Squeezes Means I'm OK

A spanking can create its own intense world for the receiver. Sometimes the giver will want to check on the receiver's well-being without asking a direct verbal question – doing so could spoil the mood, also receivers sometimes "go under" into a deep, non-verbal part of themselves. ♥ A very effective alternative to checking in verbally is for the giver to take the receiver's hand in theirs and give it two firm and noticeable, but not painful, squeezes. Each squeeze should last about one second and there should be about a one-second pause in between them. This is understood to ask the question, "Are you *basically* OK with what's going on here?" The receiver signals back that they are (at least) basically OK with the situation by giving the hand of the spanker two squeezes in return. (It is, of course, essential that you and your partner get clear on this point *before* the spanking actually begins.) ♥ If the spanker squeezes the receiver's hand and gets no reply, they should wait about ten seconds and then repeat the two squeezes. If another ten seconds brings no "reply squeezes," it's time to make verbal contact.

Spanking Trick 10

Spankings And Orgasms

If the receiver or giver is new to spanking, a considerate (and enlightened) "mentor" will make sure that the novice has at least one orgasm during or immediately after the spanking session.

Spanking Trick 11

Masturbation During Spanking

If circumstances are right, your partner can have an extremely powerful orgasm if you spank them while they masturbate. It's also possible to spank them with one hand while you masturbate them with the other. (I suppose it's hypothetically possible for you to spank them while you perform oral sex on them, but it sounds risky to me.)

Spanking Trick 12

Intercourse During Spanking

Spanking is sometimes possible during intercourse. Two positions seem to work especially well: Missionary position intercourse (with the person on top getting spanked), and doggie-style intercourse (with the person in front getting spanked). Sometimes the possibilities are adequate in other positions as well.

Spanking Trick 13

Vary The Sensation

Spanking can be alternated with exposing the buttocks to other textures. As one example, consider the sensation generated by giving the buttocks several sharp spanks, and then following them with several seconds of lightly stroking the buttocks with a piece of fake fur. (This is an almost-guaranteed "gasp producer.")

Some Final Comments On Erotic Pain Play

As a rule, the more sexually aroused somebody is, the more likely they are to be receptive to giving or receiving erotic pain. Indeed, according to the Kinsey studies, erotic pain of some type or another is part of "ordinary" love-making for nearly *half* the population, and has been for a very, very long time.

While most folks are not interested in something as "extreme" as spanking or being spanked, many people like to bite or be bitten, pinch their partner's nipples or have their own pinched, scratch or be scratched, hold their partner down during sex or be held down, and so forth.

Given that the definition of "ordinary" sex is in a state of flux, I believe that erotic pain play of *all* types must only take place after it is pre-negotiated and agreed upon, with a safe word in place and with other basic precautions taken. Otherwise, it is just too easy for confusion and misunderstandings, or worse, to occur.

I am entirely clear on the fundamental, basic differences between nonconsensual, damaging abuse and consensual, enhancing, erotic pain play. (Indeed, I donate a portion of my income to a battered women's shelter and another portion to a counseling program for batterers.)

It is not my intention to contribute in any way to the abuse, subjugation, or dehumanization of anyone. Indeed, I fully believe that this section will help to highlight the difference between abuse and erotic pain play, and make it significantly more difficult for abusers to rationalize or justify their actions – both to those they abuse and to themselves. The Bible says, "He who doeth evil hateth the light." I hope, and believe, that my writing this section made the world an ever-so-slightly brighter place.

Condoms, Gloves, And Other Goodies

I made the rounds of my safer-sex advisors just before going to print, and here are some of the juicier tidbits of news they had to report.

1. New research is producing condoms which are thinner, more sensitive and less prone to breakage condoms. A special boon to people with latex allergies, or those who prefer oil-based lubricants, is the new style of polyurethane condoms.

2. There has been a great controversy regarding the relative effectiveness of regular plastic wrap versus microwavable plastic wrap as a shield against various sexually transmitted bugs. According to both of my advisors, the best current information is that there seems no significant difference between the two, and that they both work pretty well. One of my experts did advise sticking with a name brand.

    The microwavable brand might be a bit more porous, but only at temperatures greater than 165 degrees. As one advisor put it, "Nobody's mouth is that hot!" On the other hand, there is some reason to believe that it might be slightly less likely to break with ordinary (for our purposes, anyway) use.

3. Between the time the first "Tricks" book was published and now (about a year and a half), two of my friends – each in a separate incident, by the way – acquired a sexually transmitted disease because the condom they were using either broke or slipped off and nobody noticed that until it was too late, and no "back-up" nonoxynol-9 foam or other reserve protection was in use.

I'm sorry, but the failure rate of condoms is just too high for them to be trusted on their own. I've said it before, I'll say it again now, and I intend to repeat it many times in the future:

If you're in a situation that requires using a condom, then by definition you're in a situation that requires using *more* than a condom.

4. One of my experts reports that the use of nonoxynol-9 helps a great deal in reducing the spread of sexually transmitted diseases to women during intercourse *if* it is used less than five times a week. If it is used more often, it may inflame the vagina and thus make infection more likely. (The threshold of inflammation varies considerably from woman to woman. If your vagina becomes inflamed after fewer uses, you might wish to consider engaging in alternative practices some of the time so you can restrict your use of nonoxynol-9.)

5. Many people, men especially, complain that using a condom reduces the sensation they feel. Wise condom educators point out that using a condom doesn't *reduce* sensation so much as *change* it. This can often lead to new understanding and appreciation.

6.　I'm going to get into some trouble with the "politically correct sex police" with this comment, but I feel the need to discuss it. A current practice being taught is that of using your mouth to put a condom on your partner's penis – without letting him know you are doing that (this is sometimes called "cheeking"). It's been reported, and I believe it, that a skillful person can often accomplish this without the male recipient noticing it until afterwards.

I believe I understand the point these educators are making, but I have a (not minor) problem with this practice. I believe that honesty and trustworthiness are absolutely essential prerequisites for sex. If your male partner is not willing to agree in advance to wear a condom, then I feel it's far better to either decline to have sex with him altogether or to switch to an activity in which condom use is not so important.

"Sneaking" a condom into the sex, no matter how well-intentioned, implies that dishonesty (or, at the very least, staying silent about something important) is sometimes acceptable. Understand that I am not a naive, uninformed, or innocent person. I can follow, if not necessarily agree with, arguments which assert that doing this is sometimes necessary but, all in all, I am much more not-OK with this practice than I am OK with it.

7.　One of my consultants felt that the danger of getting HIV from a woman was being seriously underestimated. They pointed out that contact with blood containing HIV can be infectious, that vaginal blood is certainly blood, and that many, many women "spot" in between their periods.

8.   One of the benefits of covering a woman's vaginal and anal area with plastic wrap before performing oral sex on her is that it makes it possible to safely perform both cunnilingus and analingus (analingus is also called rimming). Under normal circumstances, licking a woman's anus and then licking her vagina could very easily cause her to get a vaginal infection. Plastic wrap can therefore be a wonderful "analingus enabler."

9.   The use of a combination of latex gloves and lots of lubricant does a lot to, so to speak, open up the area of anal play. Gloves are particularly useful for anal (and vaginal) exploration because they shield *fingernails.* Wearing gloves also does a lot toward making this form of erotic play acceptable to exploration.

10.   One very useful trick for combining anal and vaginal play is to "double glove" by putting on a glove (possibly with a layer of lubricant inside it, against your skin), then coating that glove with a layer of lubricant, and finally putting a second glove on over the first one. This allows you to begin with anal exploration and, when you're ready to switch over to vaginal play, simply remove the outer glove and the inner glove is ready to go.

Sex, Risk, Probability, and Political Correctness

Having sex has always been dangerous. Vaginal intercourse almost always involves at least a minimal risk of unwanted pregnancy. Throughout history the chance of picking up an incurable, fatal disease was often present. (The big specter used to be syphilis; now, of course, it's AIDS.) And let's not even begin to get into how introducing sex into a previously nonsexual relationship can cause massive social uproar.

About ten years ago, having sex suddenly became a lot more dangerous than it had been for quite some time. The re-emergence of a fatal, incurable, sexually transmitted disease has once again changed the very fabric of how we live – and will continue to change it for decades.

People want to know how they can have sex and yet protect themselves. Various authorities respond with this or that regimen. Some regimens are excellent; some are a crime.

What I don't think is made clear enough to those seeking information is that essentially all of this is a matter of probabilities. No complication occurs 100% of the time, and no protective measure is 100% effective. It's all a case of shifting the odds. Granted, in many cases the odds can and should be shifted, but we need to make it clearer to people than we do that it's still a matter of probability. We see some signs of this by the emergence of the term "safer sex" to replace the somewhat misleading "safe sex."

"Political Correctness" has helped complicate things. Early in the AIDS crisis, when the modes of disease transmission were less well understood than they are today, various authorities advocated nothing less than "total body fluid isolation" rules. Bedrooms all over America began to resemble hospital "protective isolation" wards.

Today, certain practices – oral sex, in particular – are believed to be considerably less risky than previously thought. Unfortunately, no authority can recommend less than total body fluid isolation without becoming vulnerable to accusations of reckless irresponsibility by their more conservative peers. They therefore keep silent even though they might like to speak up. Taking a politically incorrect position, even if the data supports it, can ruin a career.

And, to be fair, these more conservative peers have some merit in what they say. While the odds seem sharply against it, you most definitely can become infected with the AIDS virus by performing only a single act of oral sex on an HIV+ person. Some authorities even assert you risk infection if this person performs oral sex on you.

(By the way, it also now seems that unprotected anal sex is considerably *more* risky than previously thought.)

Add into this mess that the usual medical experiments to study infectious disease cannot, for ethical reasons, be conducted, plus the new strains of virus which are emerging, and you have a genuinely murky situation. For example, we know that nonoxynol-9 kills the AIDS virus, and there's reason to believe that people who use only nonoxynol-9 to protect themselves against AIDS have a noticeably lower rate of becoming infected than those who use nothing, but no truly accurate estimates of exactly how much protection nonoxynol-9 provides seem to exist. Furthermore, finding out may be impossible.

As a finishing touch, add in the numerous personal, economic, social, political, and religious influences. The situation's clarity now drops to near zero.

So what *do* you do? Stop and think. Ask various authorities for information. Ask them (and yourself) how reliable and complete is the information on which they're basing their decisions and recommendations. Be sure to consider any hidden agendas, particularly any political or religious agendas, this authority may have.

Have you had an AIDS antibody test? This is one of the most responsible steps you can take. If you've had any unsafe contacts, have you had a test since then? Do you really understand what information such a test does and does not provide?

Has the person you're considering having sex with had such a test? How reliable is their answer likely to be? Many, many people will lie right to your face if doing so will get you to have sex with them, particularly if their chance seems close.

As it stands now, masturbating your partner seems very safe – and a skillfully administered hand job can be one of the most intense sexual experiences possible. Combine it with a lubricant containing nonoxynol-9 and the absence of any openings in the skin on your hands or their genitals and you're almost as safe as you can get. While I imagine it's happened in a few cases, I personally have never heard of anyone getting infected or becoming pregnant from using a lubricant containing nonoxynol-9 to masturbate or be masturbated by their partner.

Oral sex seems "relatively" safe. Pregnancy is almost unheard of, and it's been reliably documented that saliva neutralizes the AIDS virus. Still, some risk is involved. Please understand clearly that gonorrhea, syphilis, herpes, and other diseases can be transmitted this way (in both directions). Furthermore, the risk of getting AIDS, while small, does exist.

Vaginal sex is, of course, definitely risky. The risk of unplanned pregnancy and sexually transmitted disease is almost always present. Please be very, very careful about how and with whom you have vaginal intercourse.

Receptive anal sex seems to be, in terms of getting AIDS, the riskiest form of sex you can have these days. (The active role is not risk-free either.) A physician told me that the odds of getting infected by having a single act of unprotected, receptive anal sex with an HIV+ partner were a staggering one chance in three.

As you can see, sex involves more risk than ever before. Make sure you've had a recent antibody test. Pick your partners carefully; remember, even normally honest people will lie, particularly during "the heat of passion," if doing so will get you to have sex with them.

Choosing which acts you'll participate in definitely helps shift the odds in your favor. Using nonoxynol-9 also shifts them. A condom, provided it's used properly, adds considerable protection. Dental dams and latex gloves play crucial roles.

There is no such thing as risk-free sex. Still, as with driving a car, flying a plane, or swimming, you can reduce the odds to a level where most people consider the risk acceptable. You, of course, must decide where that level is for you. (Whatever you do, don't let another person make this decision for you.) Remember, nothing is 100% dangerous and nothing is 100% safe. Also remember that VD clinics, pregnancy crisis centers, and AIDS wards are filled with people who insisted on blinding themselves to the full extent of the risks they took.

We live in an age where sixty seconds of clear thinking about what is proper sexual behavior for you can add sixty years to your life.

About Nonoxynol-9

Laboratory evidence has shown that nonoxynol-9 can kill, not only the AIDS virus, but also the herpes virus and the infectious bugs that cause gonorrhea, syphilis, and many other sexually transmitted diseases. Nonoxynol-9 is found in, among other things, lubricants, contraceptive foams, spermicidal suppositories, contraceptive sponges, and diaper wipes. While opinions vary, two different sources told me a 1% concentration is adequate for ordinary (non-contraceptive) use. Other sources recommend higher concentrations. Most contraceptive gels intended for use with a diaphragm are in the 2% range. The lowest concentration I found in a gel intended for use without either a condom or diaphragm was 3%.

The minimal "therapeutic dose" seems to be about 150 mg. (milligrams) of nonoxynol-9. This is the dose found in the average suppository, syringe of foam, and so forth.

Somewhere between 5% to 10% of people seem to be sensitive to nonoxynol-9 and develop some degree of irritation with its use. However, please notice that this data can also be interpreted to mean that 90% to 95% of the population can use it without difficulty. Many people apparently sensitive to one particular product containing nonoxynol-9 have no problems with a different brand. Their sensitivity is often due to another component of the product, not the nonoxynol-9 itself.

Some "cousins," octoxynol-9 and nonoxynol-15, are also marketed as spermicides. My sources tell me that they too are effective bug-killers. Consider them if you have a problem with nonoxynol-9.

Nonoxynol-9 does not offer complete protection, but if it were to be more widely used I'm convinced the rate of unplanned pregnancy and sexually transmitted disease would significantly drop. This option deserves more publicity and use than it gets.

Lubricants - Advantages, Disadvantages, And Dangers

I decided not to include sex toys such as vibrators and so on in this book. Doing so would have made it much larger, and made the audience narrower. I've dealt with such topics in a separate book.

Lubricants, creams, gels, and so forth are one category of "adjuncts" to erotic play that I will discuss. In addition to adding (often very considerably) to the pleasure of those involved, lubricants can help prevent pregnancy, relieve vaginal dryness, and reduce the spread of sexually transmitted diseases, so they merit discussion in this book. Some menthol-containing lubricants cause a distinctly "hot" sensation when applied to the genitals, so some people use them for erotic play. I've discussed such lubricants in the first "Tricks" book.

Almost all lubricants can be grouped into one of two basic categories: oil-based and water-based. Oil-based lubricants generally stay slippery considerably longer than water-based lubricants. Unfortunately, these days they have a major, life-threatening property: oil-based lubricants rapidly dissolve latex. Therefore, any latex product that gets smeared with an oil-based lubricant will fall apart much sooner than it otherwise would.

If you are in a situation where you need to use a latex condom or other latex protective device, keep oil-based lubricants away from it.

The single most important thing you need to know about a lubricant is whether it is water-based or oil-based. If you are not 100% sure, you would be very wise to assume that it's oil-based and treat it accordingly.

The next most important thing you need to know about a lubricant is whether or not it contains nonoxynol-9. Some people believe that only water-based lubricants contain nonoxynol-9 and, therefore, believe that if they buy a lubricant containing nonoxynol-9 they are automatically buying a water-based lubricant. This is simply not true. While most oil-based lubricants do not contain nonoxynol-9, I know of at least two different brands that do. Water-based lubricants usually plainly state that fact. Read the label carefully.

If you can, find out what percentage of nonoxynol-9 is present. Ordinary lubricants typically contain about 1% (and usually don't state the percentage on the label). Contraceptive gels tend to run 2% or a bit higher.

I have long believed that nonoxynol-9 should be used more widely than it is now. Most people can use it with no problems, and it contributes a lot toward helping to fight unplanned pregnancy and sexually transmitted disease.

Water-based lubes can be used with condoms and other devices, but they tend to dry out and get "sticky" much more quickly than oil-based lubes. Therefore, smart players keep a small supply of water close by. This can either be something like a "finger bowl" or a separate bottle just for holding water. Sometimes the lubricant-containing bottle and the water-containing bottle are glued or taped together so one doesn't get quite so easily "lost." One caution: When you need to add water, add only a very few drops. You can, for all practical purposes, wash the lubricant (and its benefits) away if you add too much water. Every now and then add more lubricant instead of adding more water.

Supplemental Thought: Your saliva can also be used to "help loosen up" the lubricant, and contact with saliva reduces the infectivity of the AIDS virus. Welcome this extra protection, but definitely don't rely on it. *Another Supplemental Thought:* A physician told me some evidence exists that the use of any lubricant might (repeat, might) reduce the possibility of passing on a sexually transmitted disease. The thinking is that, because lubricants reduce the amount of "wear and tear" on the body parts involved, fewer breaks in the skin get created, and thus the probability of at least some forms of disease transmission is reduced. (Other bugs, of course, go right through intact skin with no problem at all.) As with the information about saliva noted above, welcome this extra protection, but absolutely do not rely on it.

A visit to your local drugstore, adult bookstore, or erotic boutique will help acquaint you with, among others, such names as Astroglide, Probe, Slippery Stuff, KY Jelly, PrePair, ForPlay, and Wet. (You should also look over their selection of condoms, contraceptive gels, spermicidal suppositories, and so forth.)

Your local drugstore may also have some additional, unexpected treasures. A liquefying cleanser called Albolene has enjoyed a semi-underground following for years as an excellent lubricant for erotic play, particularly masturbation. At some sex parties, you get a discount on your admission fee if you bring a jar – a sort of BYOA situation. One caution: Albolene is oil-based and doesn't contain nonoxynol-9, so consider carefully when to use it .

Other "non-traditional" lubricants include Johnson's Baby Magic Lotion, Crisco, coconut oil (one of my favorites), vegetable oil, and petroleum jelly. These all share Albolene's limits.

A carefully chosen lubricant can add considerable safety and pleasure to your erotic play. Make sure you clearly understand the advantages and disadvantages of each type.

What To Do If A Condom Fails

OK, guy, while having vaginal intercourse you look down and you see that the condom you were wearing has broken and you are now wearing a small latex ring around the base of your cock. Or maybe you look down and discover that the condom is gone. (You were thinking that this particular brand caused very little loss of sensation.) Perhaps you have already come. What do you do now?

STOP! Then, first of all, if she doesn't already know, you gotta tell her. Try not to sound too alarmed (she may regard what has happened as a big deal, or she may not), but let her know what happened.

OK, you told her. Now what? If you're worried about getting a sexually transmitted disease, go into the bathroom and wash your genitals several times with very generous amounts of soap and water, then empty your bladder (and maybe drink fluids so you can "flush out" your urethra some more). One nurse who worked in a VD clinic told me that washing and urinating shortly after sex would reduce a man's chances of getting gonorrhea by 50%. (She had no information about whether doing this reduced his chances of getting other diseases.) Another nurse, who also works in a VD clinic, told me that she spends a lot of her time treating "that unlucky 50%" of the men who had tried doing this and it didn't work.

If you weren't already using a lubricant containing nonoxynol- 9, but have some handy, consider applying a liberal amount to your genitals and the surrounding areas. Let it sit there for five to ten minutes before washing it off. Nonoxynol-9 can kill the bugs that cause AIDS, herpes, syphilis, gonorrhea, and many other diseases, so giving it a chance to help makes sense to me.

This could be overkill, but after you wash, consider applying rubbing alcohol, hydrogen peroxide, or an antiseptic (Betadine, or a generic version of it, would be a good choice) as a final touch.

What about her? A woman is in a riskier situation. Trying to wash out your semen (and whatever it contains) may drive some of it further up into her body. Therefore, consider immediately inserting two spermicidal suppositories into her vagina. This will place a considerable amount of nonoxynol-9 into her without driving whatever's already in there further in (as the pressure caused by using a syringe full of contraceptive foam might).

Once the suppositories have had a chance to work (15 minutes?), then she can wash herself off, and out. Opinions differ as to whether or not douching is a good idea. While you're waiting, nonoxynol-9 can be applied to her external genital region, and washed off later, to help zap any bugs or sperm lurking there. Urinating may also help.

Again, this may be overkill, but I'll point out that it's possible to douche with a dilute Betadine-type solution. Also, as with men, rubbing alcohol, hydrogen peroxide, and antiseptic creams can be applied to the external genitals.

If you feel you need immediate advice, call your doctor or a clinic. If it's late at night (when these events tend to happen), consider calling a hospital emergency room. They won't consider such a call out of line.

In the morning, it's crucial (repeat, crucial) that you call your regular doctor, a local VD clinic, or family planning center for advice. They may want you to come in, either that day or within a day or two, for an examination. Among other things, if you're worried about getting pregnant they can arrange for you to get a "morning after" pill.

Perhaps the most important point of this essay is to point out, once again, that a condom by itself is not adequate protection. Their failure rate is simply too high and, if you're not using anything else, you may not notice such a failure until it's too late.

Remember, if you're in a situation where you need to use a condom, then by definition you're in a situation where you need to use *more* than a condom.

What To Do for a Contaminated Skin Break

In these hazardous times, it's possible for you to get an unwelcome "splash" of potentially infectious semen, blood, urine, fecal matter, or vaginal fluid upon your body. It this occurs on unbroken skin, you're probably not facing much risk – provided you wash it off quickly.

On the other hand, if you get "splashed" on a break in your skin, or in your mouth, or your eye, or on your genital or anal area, you could be facing a very real risk of becoming infected.

It's a myth that "it only takes one" germ or virus or fungus to contract a contagious disease. (If it were true, none of us would live even a week after birth, for we are all contaminated all the time.) In fact, it usually takes several million of the little beasts to give us a disease. Medical folks call this an "infectious concentration."

Therefore, if you do get splashed, the most important thing you can do is to clean yourself off *right away*. Don't delay this. Not even for one minute. Take care of it *now!* This is your one major opportunity to reduce the number of bugs entering your body to below infectious concentration levels.

You have two basic tactics: (1) Physical removal of the bugs. (2) Killing as many of them as possible (or possibly rendering them non-infective). Of the two, physical removal usually works best.

For example, let's say some semen splashes onto a bad scratch on one of your hands. Wipe it on your clothing, or a towel, or even on your unbroken skin, as you head for the faucet. Get your hand under briskly running water immediately. Wash it with soap if you have some.

If you have rubbing alcohol, or hydrogen peroxide, or a provodone-iodine solution such as Betadine handy (and you should), employ it at once. Do whatever you can, as quickly as you can, to get as much of that infectious fluid off of you as fast as possible. Among other things, saliva is believed to help render the HIV virus non-infective, so it may be entirely rational to spit on the wound, wipe, and spit again.

If something splashes into your mouth, maybe you can immediately use an alcohol-containing mouthwash. Rinsing your mouth out with a strong liquor might be very wise. Some folks think that rinsing your mouth out with hydrogen peroxide is a good idea. (For goodness sake, don't actually swallow any of these solutions.)

If none of these is available to rinse out your mouth, keep in mind that carbonated soft drinks are highly acidic and can kill bugs.

If something splashes into your eye, avoid any of the strong materials mentioned above. Flush your eye with lukewarm water, and plenty of it, repeatedly.

For cleaning the genital/anal area, see the "What to do if A Condom Fails" section.

Once you have cleaned yourself off as much as you can, there is little else you can do immediately other than perhaps to cover any possibly contaminated skin breaks with a disinfectant liquid or cream. Betadine, or its generic equivalent, would be my first choice.

The next step, and it's *very* important, is to visit a physician within the next 24 hours. (It's probably not essential to go there at once if it's the middle of the night, but definitely go the next day.) Tell them what happened, and what emergency measures you took. They may want to test your blood for the existence of any infection you might already have. Any new infection will take at least a few days, and maybe a few months, to show itself. They may want to take other measures. Each case is different. *Remember* It's very important to see a physician within 24 hours of the possible exposure.

Finally, let us not forget the importance of preventing such an incident in the first place. While accidental splashes in the mouth or eyes are rare (and we probably don't need to start wearing those face shields that many doctors and dentists wear), we do need to start being more careful about exposing our skin, particularly any breaks in our skin.

Our hands seem most at risk. They're often very near "where the action is" and any break in them can be terribly dangerous. Here are two suggestions.

First, if you're going to play with a possibly infectious person (and such a person can be the very picture of youthful, vibrant health) you might first test the skin around your hands for small breaks. Spreading some rubbing alcohol on your hands is often very effective at revealing breaks. (Vinegar works even better, but its use is not always appropriate.)

Second, latex gloves are readily available and cheap. I've carried some in my jacket for years, and they've proven useful on a number of occasions (I change them every six months or so. They get weak with prolonged storage.) Unless you are absolutely sure that your partner is not infected, *wear those gloves.*

A Warning About SM

The following is closely based on material in "SM 101: A Realistic Introduction."

SM is the riskiest form of sex. In addition to all the dangers of regular "vanilla" sex (unwanted pregnancy, sexually transmitted disease, and so forth), considerable danger of physical injury and/or emotional trauma exists. Furthermore, the abuse potential of a situation in which one person is tied up and at the mercy of another is dreadful to contemplate.

SM is not so dangerous that it should be avoided altogether, but, like skydiving, mountain climbing, and auto racing, people must learn about its risks, and learn about how to deal with them, before getting involved. That is not happening anywhere near as much as it should. A recent article in the San Francisco *Chronicle* mentioned that 25% of all adults have at least experimented with bondage. Only a tiny percentage of such people receive adequate instruction.

Therefore, I have included some of the most basic SM safety teachings in this book. Such instruction is far, far from complete, but will help guide you away from the major danger areas. I have also included the addresses of a few of the larger and better known SM clubs around the country. I cannot overstress how important it is to get proper instruction, and learn the proper perspective and context for SM play, from qualified people. Your life may literally depend on it.

I need to add that the image of SM presented in most "adult" videos, books, and magazines has usually been terribly inaccurate and irresponsible. A very few are excellent. Most are dangerous, irresponsible crap.

I have written a very comprehensive book about SM's basic techniques and safety measures. It's carried at many leather stores and erotic boutiques across the country. If you have such a store near you, please see if they carry it. If they don't, send a self-addressed, stamped envelope to Greenery Press at 3739 Balboa Ave. #195, San Francisco, CA 94121, for information about how to buy it directly. I, and probably the store, would also appreciate it if you would give them this address.

The fundamental teaching of SM is that it is consensual. Both parties agree to participate, and either party has the right to stop the activity for any reason whatsoever. Refusing to untie someone who has demanded to be untied is a serious crime. Remember, if it's not completely consensual, then it's rape.

The Tricks most relevant to SM from the first "Tricks" book are listed here.

·:· 50 ·:·

Bondage Safety Tip #1: Loss Of Sensation

There is never any need to tie any body part so tightly that it loses feeling. If some part of your lover's body "goes to sleep," then it's time to loosen whatever's causing the problem.

· · · · · ·
·51·
· · · · · ·

Bondage Safety Tip #2: Quick Release

If you tie someone up, you must have some method of releasing them quickly. That means you must be able to get them completely free within sixty seconds, and preferably within thirty seconds. ♥ One basic safety precaution is to keep a pair of scissors handy so you can cut your lover free in an emergency like a fire or earthquake. The large, plastic-handled "paramedic scissors" popular with rescue squads are an excellent choice because, unlike regular bandage scissors, they were designed to cut through leather, webbing, and other heavy materials quickly. These scissors are available at many medical supply stores. The more health-conscious and responsible leather stores and erotic boutiques also carry them. ♥ Both nylon stockings and silk scarves – often the first choice of beginners –are notoriously difficult to untie if the knots have been pulled really tight Don't use anything you're not willing to cut through if necessary.

· · · · · ·
·52·
· · · · · ·

Bondage Safety Tip #3: Stay With Them

Many people think it would be fun to "tie them up and then go off and leave them." In fact, this is one of the most dangerous, irresponsible things you can do. It's a crime in many areas. Furthermore, if your partner is injured in any way while you are gone, even if they asked you to leave them, you could face major criminal charges. ♥ Here's a simple rule: Always stay as close to a bound person, and check on them as often, as you would an infant left in your care. If you gag them, stay even closer and check even more often.

:53:

Bondage Safety Tip #4: Emergency Lighting

A bound person needs to be closely watched. In an emergency, they need to be immediately freed. To do both of these in an efficient manner, you need light. A power failure during a normal sexual encounter can be, at the least, annoying. A power failure during a bondage session can be a serious, even life-threatening, problem. ♥ Therefore, responsible bondage fans always make sure they have emergency light sources immediately available. Flashlights, especially light-colored ones that are easy to see, are carried in pockets, stored in specific places in "toy bags," and otherwise placed where they can be easily found in the dark. ♥ Furthermore, increasing numbers of bedrooms and "playrooms" now have "blackout lights" – lights that come on automatically if the power fails – plugged into their wall sockets. Basic models that will do quite nicely for the average-sized room can be bought at drugstores, variety stores, and similar places for around ten to twenty dollars.

The Dangers of Self-Bondage

Many people have bondage fantasies but no partner, so they bind themselves. The person interested in self-bondage faces a problem. They want to bind themselves so they can't escape, yet, obviously, eventually they will want release. What to do?

Self-bondage can be extremely dangerous. You know how risky it is to bind someone and then leave them alone. The self-bound person has this obvious problem.

I have heard of several deaths resulting from self-bondage that went wrong. Even more disturbing, many of these deaths involved highly experienced players who "knew what they were doing" yet died anyway. Most such fatalities involved gags, hoods, ropes around the neck, or some other devices that had the potential to restrict breathing.

Most self-bondage involves locking devices, especially around the wrists. The person works out some mechanism by which the keys again come within their grasp. If the device fails to work (and, sooner or later, it will fail) the self-bound person often has no other way to get free or summon help.

Also of critical importance, bondage not tight enough to quickly put the bound area to sleep may still be tight enough to do that gradually. The self-bound person's hands may go numb after an hour. If the keys fall within reach after that – trouble.

I experimented for a while with self-bondage, but gave it up after I had an incident that gave me a moment of nearly pure panic. I also found that, besides its dangers, self-bondage has other drawbacks.

First, you may rapidly discover that being in bondage without a "sweet tormentor" for company is *boring*. The vibrators, clamps, dildoes, and other gear that aroused you when you first put yourself in bondage may feel awful after your arousal fades – even if it doesn't malfunction or go out of adjustment. If, genius that you are, you set the situation up so you can't get loose for three hours, you may find that the last two hours and fifty minutes go on for a *very* long time.

You might try binding your breasts and genitals, but be very conservative about using anything that would restrict your breathing (gags, hoods, neck ropes), make you vulnerable to a fall (blindfolds) or restrict your limbs – especially your arms.

Self-bondage often seems like a good idea in fantasy, and offers plausible exploration, as long as *absolutely nothing* goes wrong. Remember that even a minor maladjustment of a piece of equipment can set the stage for hours of genuine suffering, and that a serious malfunction or unexpected development can cause you to die a slow, agonizing death. Many "experts" died exactly this way.

SM Clubs

The largest and best-known clubs in the United States are listed under "Sadomasochism" on p. 115. If you don't live near one, ask for a referral to a nearer club. Also, some of these clubs put out highly informative newsletters. You might therefore want to join anyway so you can receive them.

An Even Stronger Warning About Breath Control Play

(The following is an excerpt from my book "SM 101: A Realistic Introduction.")

Some people explore choking, suffocation, and other forms of "breath control." Why? Well, the first symptom of oxygen deprivation is often euphoria. Also, the idea of this degree of control can be compelling: one submissive woman gasped with wonder (and delight) when she considered that her master might "control the very air I breathe." Unfortunately, this area is the single most dangerous aspect of SM-related play.

After a great deal of investigation, consideration, and discussing this subject with people who have much more medical knowledge than I have, I have been unable to learn any way to make breath control play acceptably safe. Furthermore, the overwhelming majority of the SM-related fatalities I have heard of were related to restricting breathing.

The whole problem lies in determining how much is enough. It's similar to the old mechanic's joke: How tight should I tighten this bolt?... Tighten it up to a quarter-turn before it strips.

The goal of some forms of breath control play seems to be to render someone unconscious and then revive them. Unfortunately, the means used to render the person unconscious by interfering with the amount of oxygen to their brain also, and unknown by many people, affects their heart.

People usually appear to tolerate this well, but if there's a mishap – they die. Another serious problem is that every episode of unconsciousness seems to cause at least some permanent (repeat, *permanent*) brain damage.

There simply seems to be no safe way to play in this area. Police "judo chokes" designed to cause harmless unconsciousness have been banned by many departments because these holds caused deaths in many cases, sometimes hours after the choke was applied. "Experts" at breath-control-related erotic play have died because their "failsafe" devices failed. Even apparently safe practices such as ordering the submissive to hold their own breath or ordering them to hyperventilate can be far riskier than they seem to be.

"Auto-erotic asphyxiation" masturbation games cause hundreds of fatalities in otherwise healthy people each year. I was once involved in a resuscitation attempt on such a case during my ambulance days. I still remember my partner, myself, the cops, the fire department, and the hospital emergency room crew doing the best CPR we could on a young teenage boy while his mother yelled and screamed and prayed frantically to God to please, please, please not take her boy. (We got his heart going again, but he died the next day.)

I have researched this area a great deal, and I find no acceptably safe way to play with it. I have listened carefully to several "experts," and I've found alarming flaws in their reasoning and deficits in their knowledge. I have read literature associated with breath control play, and it also scares me. Stay away from this stuff.

Footnote: Because I hate to say that any erotic practice is so dangerous that it should never be done, I'm willing to listen further to advocates of breath control play. However, I've listened to some, and so far they have not only failed to impress me – they have appalled me.

You can write to me about how you think breath control play can be safely done if you want – but if you don't have a clear, detailed understanding of arterial blood gases, PVCs, the vagus nerve, asystole, syncope, acetylcholine, hypocarbia, tetany, ventricular fibrillation, and related subjects then you have absolutely no business telling anybody anything about breath control play other than to stay away from it.

Problems

Probably the most important advice I can give you regarding finding help for the problems listed below, and other problems, is to grab your phone book and start looking. Many communities have local resources. Check the first few pages and look over the table of contents. Look up these and related topics in both the white and yellow pages. Check your phone book for an index.

If this doesn't help much, go to your local library and look through the phone books of nearby communities, particularly those of nearby big cities.

Local newspapers and magazines, particular free or low-cost ones that come out on a weekly or less frequent basis, often carry valuable listings. Gay and lesbian papers can be particularly helpful. Look them over carefully.

The internet is an excellent source of information regarding sexuality-related problems. Look in the alt.recovery, alt.sex and alt.support hierarchies, and in any newsgroups that announce local events and groups in your community.

Abuse/Battering/Neglect

National Domestic Violence Hotline (800) 333-SAFE

National Child Abuse Hotline (800) 422-4453

Parents Anonymous (800) 421-0353

AIDS

National AIDS Hotline (800) 342-AIDS

National STD Hotline (800) 227-8922

Birth Control/Abortion
Check your local yellow pages under "Birth Control Information Centers." Note: Some anti-abortion agencies have been accused of being less than totally honest about that fact. If a given resource doesn't explicitly say that it offers abortions, please consider that its policies may be anti-abortion.

Censorship

American Civil Liberties Union
132 West 43rd St.
New York, New York 10036

National Coalition Against Censorship
132 West 43rd. Street
New York, New York 10036
(212) 944-9899

People for the American Way
2000 M. Street N.W., Suite 400
Washington, DC 20036
(202) 467-4999

Death During Sex
People, especially older men, die during sex far more often than is commonly believed. One of the reasons for this is that their partners are often too embarrassed to tell what was going on when the death occurred.

Studies have shown that the person in the community who faces the highest risk of sudden cardiac arrest is a man over the age of 50, and the person most likely to be with him when it happens is his wife. If your boyfriend or husband is over 50, I strongly recommend that you schedule such training.

Studies have also shown that the second highest risk group for a sudden cardiopulmonary emergency is, to simplify matters, anyone wearing diapers. If you help take care of young children, schedule a class that teaches infant and child CPR. (The technique differs considerably from that used on adults.)

You can look in the yellow pages under "First Aid Instruction" to find out where classes are offered. The American Red Cross, American Heart Association, some hospitals and emergency service agencies, and private firms all offer classes.

If you take a CPR class, try hard to get a good instructor. I suggest someone who has a minimum of one year of full-time experience in pre-hospital emergency care. A paramedic might be a good first choice. (Although people who are good at providing emergency care are not necessarily good at teaching others how to do that.)

Disabilities

The Lawrence Research Group, which publishes the Xandria Collection catalogs, puts out a specialized catalog of sex toys and advice for people with disabilities. This catalog also contains a page listing of sexuality resources for the disabled across the U.S. To receive this catalog, send $4 and a request for the Special Edition for Disabled People to:

Lawrence Research Group
P.O. Box 319005
San Francisco, CA   94131

Herpes

Herpes Resource Center (HRC)
P.O. Box 13827
Research Triangle Park, North Carolina 27709

These folks offer wonderful information for those coping with any aspect of herpes. Among other things, they sponsor a nationwide network of support groups. If somebody I cared about had herpes, I would make certain that they were fully informed about what these folks offer.

National STD Hotline (800) 227-8922

Incest

Incest Survivors Anonymous
P.O. Box 5613
Long Beach, CA 90805-0613
(310) 428-5599

Survivors of Incest Anonymous
P.O. Box 21817
Baltimore, Maryland 21222
(410) 433-2365

Both of these groups sponsor meetings all over the country. They will also help you start a group in your area if one does not already exist. Incest is one of the most under-reported forms of abuse in this country.

Old Age

Sex Over Forty Newsletter
PHE, Inc.
P.O. Box 1600
Chapel Hill, North Carolina 27515

As people age, their needs and their bodies change. This newsletter is one of the most informative and useful sources of information on the topic.

Rape

As soon as you safely can, call 911, a rape treatment center, or a similar resource. Check your phone book under Rape,

Battering, and Sexual Abuse Aid. It's very important from a medical, emotional, and legal point of view to seek help as soon as possible after the assault.

Know that an attempted rape can be almost as damaging, and take as long to recover from, as a completed rape. If you can safely do so, have the authorities come to the scene so they can look for valuable evidence. Try not to shower, douche, brush your teeth, or change clothes until you've been examined.

If you need support or don't feel your case is being handled properly, by all means contact a rape crisis center for more help.

Sex Therapy

You don't necessarily need a formally trained sex therapist to help you cope with sexual problems. Many therapists with broader training do excellent work in this field.

That said, I want to mention that the organizations listed below help train and set policies for sex therapists. Someone representing themselves as a sex therapist would probably have extensive contact with at least one of them.

Sex therapy is not an exact science. In particular, such issues as the use of surrogates are highly controversial. You should understand that the organizations listed below are far from in total agreement on every issue. AASECT is considered the more conservative.

Society for the Scientific Study of Sex (SSSS)
P.O. Box 208
Mount Vernon, Iowa, 52314

American Association of Sex Educators, Counselors, and Therapists (AASECT)
435 Michigan Ave, Suite 1717
Chicago, Illinois 60611

Sex and Love Addiction

These are 12-step groups designed to help people achieve "sexual sobriety" by using the principles of Alcoholics Anonymous. They have chapters in many parts of the country. If one doesn't exist in your area, they will help you start one. (Don't be surprised if your initial outreach efforts draw more people than you expected.)

Sexaholics Anonymous
P.O. Box 300
Simi Valley, CA 93062

Sex and Love Addicts Anonymous
P.O. Box 119
New Town Branch
Boston MA 02258

Suicidal/Homicidal Feelings

Almost every local community has telephone crisis hotlines. Again, check your telephone book – particularly the first few pages.

Additional Resource Information

The organizations listed below offer referrals and a sympathetic ear. They most definitely do not, however, offer phone sex.

San Francisco Sex Information (415) 621-7300

Los Angeles Sex Information (213) 653-1123

Alternative Sexuality Resources

As with the "Problems" section, many resources can be found by carefully checking in your phone book and by visiting the library to check the phone books of nearby cities, particularly large ones. Also, many alternative sexuality clubs and other resources advertise in adult papers and other periodicals with an erotic slant.

The internet is also an excellent source of information regarding most forms of alternative sexuality. The majority of sexuality newsgroups fall under the alt.sex hierarchy, but some, typically more oriented toward philosophy, politics and discussion, can also be found in other hierarchies such as soc.*.

Important Notice: When writing to any of these organizations, it's wise to include a business-sized, self-addressed, stamped envelope.

Bisexuality
Bisexual Resource Center
Robyn Ochs
P.O. Box 639
Cambridge, MA 02140
(617) 338-9595

Body Size and Weight

National Organization to Advance Fat Acceptance (NAAFA)
P.O. Box 188630
Sacramento, CA 95818
A national support organization, with chapters in many cities, for fat people and their admirers.

Corsetry

For people who enjoy wearing corsets and people who enjoy people who enjoy wearing corsets.

B.R. Creations
P.O. Box 4201
Mountain View, CA 94040
Ask about their "Corset Newsletter."

Cross Dressing
ETVC
P.O. Box 426486
San Francisco, CA 94142
This is a respected educational and social organization for people exploring gender issues and those who care about them. It publishes a newsletter that contains many local resources, national resources, and information on other local groups around the country. Highly recommended.

International Foundation for Gender Education (I.F.G.E.)
P.O. Box 367
Wayland, MA 01778
(617) 894-8340
The organization publishes the "TV/TS Tapestry Journal. A 150+ page magazine containing articles, references and other resources. Sample copy $12.00. Again, highly recommended.

Expanded Families

PEP
Box 6306
Captain Cook, Hawaii 96704-6306
Nationwide organization promoting polyfidelity, group marriage, and expanded families.

Gay and Lesbian Resources

National Gay Yellow Pages ($10.00)
Box 292
Village Station
New York, New York 10014
Again, your local phone book should help you find resources in your area.

Infantilism

Diaper Pail Friends
38 Miller Avenue #127
Mill Valley, CA   94941
This is *not* about adults having sex with children. DPF is an organization for adults who enjoy dressing up and pretending to be babies.

Piercing, Scarification, and Other Body Modification
The following magazines contain wonderful introductory information and referrals for those who are into having more than their nose pierced. Warning: Piercing, scarification, branding, and other forms of body modification can cause injury or death if done improperly. Proper training and supervision is essential; never attempt these practices without it.

Body Play and Modern Primitives Quarterly
P.O. Box 421668
San Francisco, CA 94142-1668 Sample issue: $12.00.

Piercing Fans International Quarterly (PFIQ)
Gauntlet
8720 Santa Monica Blvd.
Los Angeles, CA 90069   Sample issue: $10.00

Penis Size, Shape, and so forth
The Hung Jury
P.O. Box 417
Los Angeles, CA 90078
A dating service for well-hung men and the women who love them.

Small, Etc.
P.O. Box 294
Bayside, New York 11361

NOCIRC (an anti-circumcision organization)
P.O. Box 2512
San Anselmo, CA 94960

Prostitute Support Groups
(Mailing addresses only. For sex workers only. No would-be customers need write!)

Coyote
2269 Chestnut Street # 452
San Francisco, CA 94123

Coyote – Los Angeles
1626 N. Wilcox Ave. # 580
Hollywood, CA 90028

Prostitutes of New York (PONY)
25 West 45th St., # 1401
New York, New York 10036

Hooking is Real Employment (HIRE)
P.O. Box 89386
Atlanta, GA 39359

Prostitutes Anonymous
11225 Magnolia Blvd. # 181
North Hollywood, CA 91601
For those who want to leave the sex industry or for help afterwards.

Swinging

This form of sexuality used to be called "wife-swapping."

North American Swing Club Association (NASCA)
P.O. Box 7128
Buena Park, CA 90622
Publishes "International Directory of Swing Clubs and Publications."

Sadomasochism

The following organizations are some of the largest. They are open to both men and women. They can provide referrals to those seeking all-male or all-female groups and to those seeking clubs closer to where they live. (Several new clubs form each year.)

Chicagoland Discussion Group
P.O. Box 25009
Chicago, Illinois 60625

Eulenspiegel Society (Believed to be the oldest SM club in the U.S.)
P.O. Box 2783 GCS
New York, New York 10163

Society of Janus
P.O. Box 426794
San Francisco, CA 94142-6794

Threshold
2554 Lincoln Blvd., # 381
Marina Del Rey, CA 90291

Tantra

Tantra, The Magazine
P.O. Box 79
Torreon, New Mexico 87061-9900
Tantra, and its cousins Quodoushka and Healing Tao, are spiritual pathways whose teachings and practices include sexuality. *Tantra, The Magazine* contains excellent listings and descriptions of classes, workshops, and other activities offered around the country.

Transgenderism
For those wishing to change their genders.

FTM (stands for Female-to-Male)
5337 College Ave. # 142
Oakland, CA 94618

San Francisco Gender Information
P.O. Box 423602
San Francisco, CA 94142

Gender Identity Center Newsletter
3715 West 32nd Ave.
Denver, CO 80211

TV/TS Tapestry Journal
Internatonal Foundation for Gender Education (IFGE)
P.O. Box 367
Wayland, MA 01778

Additional Alternative Sexuality Information
The organizations listed below offer referrals and a sympathetic ear. They most definitely do not, however, offer phone sex.

San Francisco Sex Information (415) 621-7300

Los Angeles Sex Information (213) 653-1123

Bibliography

"A New View of a Woman's Body" by The Federation of Feminist Women's Health Centers
published by Feminist Press
8235 Santa Monica Blvd., Suite 201
West Hollywood, CA 90046

"The Complete Guide to Safer Sex"
Institute for Advanced Study of Human Sexuality
1525 Franklin Street
San Francisco, CA 94109

"For Play: 150 Sex Games for Couples"
by Walter Shelburne, Ph.D.
Waterfall Press
5337 College Avenue, #139
Oakland, CA 94618

Condom Educator's Guide, Version Two
by Daniel Bao and Beowulf Thorne
Condom Resource Center
P.O. Box 30564
Oakland, CA 94604
(510) 891-0455

"Sex: A User's Manual"
by The Diagram Group

"Anal Pleasure and Health: A Guide for Men and Women" (Second Edition)
by Jack Morin, Ph.D.
Yes Press
938 Howard Street
San Francisco, CA 94103

"The New Our Bodies, Ourselves: A Book By and For Women"
by The Boston Women's Health Book Collective
A Touchstone Book
 published by Simon and Schuster

"The Good Vibrations Guide to Sex"
by Cathy Winks and Anne Semans
published by Cleis Press

"The Black Book"
edited by Bill Brent
P.O. Box 31155
San Francisco, CA 94131-0155
A comprehensive national guide to sexuality clubs, stores, publications and other resources.

Please Send Me Your Tricks (but read this carefully first)

Do you do something that consistently drives your lovers wild? Would you like to share your Trick with the rest of us? Send it to me! I plan to publish more "Tricks" books. Maybe you can be a contributor.

Send me your Trick, preferably typed on one side of a standard sheet of paper. Please date the paper and include illustrations as necessary. If I use your Trick, I'll send you a free copy of the book it appears in and, if you wish, put your name on the "thank you" list in that book. Because of "independent discovery" it's impossible for me to credit a particular person with a particular Trick. (I repeatedly encountered independent discovery while researching this book.)

Also, again because of independent discovery, I'll undoubtedly receive letters from different people describing essentially the same Trick, and I can only afford to reward the first person who clearly describes the Trick in question. So, again, please date your letter. (Actually, I'll probably send a book to the first three or so people who send in a given Trick.)

You can increase your chances of inclusion by sending more than one Trick. One per page, please. Please don't send more than ten Tricks a year. I wouldn't have time to properly consider them. Let me know what type of credit you want on the "thank you" list. You may choose between anonymous, first name only, initials only, your nickname, or your full legal name. If you wish, I can also include your city. If you sign your Trick with your full name, be honest about your identity and include your address and phone number. Signing another person's name to a letter is a crime, and I will verify all full names before publishing them.

Please send your Trick only by regular first class mail. Spare me from certified letters, registered letters, and so forth. If you don't feel you can trust me, please don't send me your Trick. Also, please don't put a copyright notice on it. A unique usage of words can be copyrighted, but not what such words describe. (This is what allows dozens of reporters to each write a story about the same incident.) Also, I'd almost undoubtedly need to re-write your words while preserving the essence of your Trick.

Please don't send anything "too far out" or dangerous. Letters dealing with children or animals will be immediately turned over to the police.

Please don't send anything regarding political issues, economic concerns, social problems, and so forth. Again, those matters deserve books of their own. (However, if you know of a widely available resource that can help someone with a personal problem closely related to sexuality, I would love to share that information with my readers.)

I was utterly unprepared for the volume of mail that resulted from the publication of my other books. This will add to my load, and I'm already chronically behind in answering that. I therefore can't promise you an individual reply. Including a self-addressed, stamped envelope will help somewhat, but please don't get your hopes up too far. Also, I won't know until just before publication whether or not your Trick was included, so please don't write and ask. You'll know very shortly after I know.

I apologize if the above seems negative and restrictive, but it reflects learning from experience. If you would be happy with a book and being on the "thank you" list, but wouldn't be too disappointed if your Trick didn't make it, then I would genuinely love to hear from you. This world can use a little more pleasure. I hope you help contribute to that.

Send your Tricks to: Jay Wiseman, c/o Greenery Press, 3739 Balboa Ave. #195, San Francisco, CA 94121.

Other Publications from Greenery Press